The
Mermaid
Reader

FRANKLIN WATTS INC., NEW YORK

The

Mermaid Reader

And of Mermen, Nixies, Water-Nymphs, Sea Sirens, Sea-Serpents, Sprites and kindred creatures of the deep.

Selected by HELEN O'CLERY

Decorations by ENRICO ARNO

international

A Word About Spelling

If as you read you suddenly should become aware that on one
page a word is written a certain way, and elsewhere it appears another way, the reason is not that your eyes are playing you tricks nor
that the proofreader has been napping. It is rather that in all the
writing from the British Isles, the original spelling has been kept.
In all the other writing, the American spelling has been used.

Acknowledgments

THE EDITOR AND THE PUBLISHER have made every effort to trace the ownership of all material contained herein. It is their belief that the necessary permissions from publishers and authors have been obtained in all cases. In the event of any questions arising as to the use of any material, the editor and publisher, while expressing regret for any error unconsciously made, will be pleased to make the necessary correction in future editions of this book.

Thanks are due the following authors, publishers, and publications who helped make this selection possible.

"Mermaids defined" from *The Encyclopedia Americana*. Copyright © 1962 by Americana Corporation in the United States of America.

v

Contents

About this Book

MERMAIDS have intrigued human beings since the beginning of thought. From all over the world we get legends of fabulous underwater dwellers, which seems to show that man everywhere is, and always has been, only too happy to believe in Mermaids.

Poets have sung of mermaids all down through the ages. Storytellers for both old and young have let their imaginations run riot on this theme. Fishermen are unshakeable in their belief in these fascinating creatures. They've *seen* them and I feel sure you have, too.

I certainly have. In the very early morning they sit on the rocks off the West coast of Ireland, and comb their hair. Why they should spend so much time combing their hair I don't know, but people who have seen them almost all agree on this point. The mermaids I saw in the cold gray dawn certainly seemed to be holding mirrors in their hands. I couldn't be sure about the combs for, as soon as they saw me looking at them, they slid gracefully into the water and disappeared.

Of course there *were* people who assured me that what I had seen were seals.

Why, even encyclopaedias, which are not given to flights of fancy, define mermaids and even list their characteristics.

When you read through this book you'll see for yourself how these strange, sometimes pathetic, always relentless mermaids take over every poem and story almost against the writer's will, as if siren voices chanted in his ears and pale green tapering fingers took possession of his pen . . .

Helen O'Clery

The

Mermaid
Reader

Mermaids Defined

O F THE LOOKS and habits of mermaids and mermen, the encyclopedias have amazing things
to tell, such as that these sea beings have no feet, but
quite another ending to their persons, that they sometimes wear the skin of seals, and that they are given to
sitting on rocks in the water and combing their long hair.
Here in part is what the *Encyclopedia Americana* has to
say:

MERMAID, *a mythical sea-dwell-
ing creature of European folklore,
resembling a woman but having a
fishtail instead of legs. Mermaids
are supposed to lure . . . men to
destruction by enticing them into the
depths of the sea; and as a correlative,
they are sometimes represented as securing their own destruction by quitting the
sea, through marriage with a human
husband. By this means they magically
obtain temporarily a complete human
form and soul, but always end in bringing disaster to one or both of the sacri-
legious pair . . .*

1

The Natural History
of Mermaids

RICHARD CARRINGTON

FOR ANY ONE who could afford to pay 6½d for a four page broadsheet consisting mainly of advertisements, *The Times* of Friday, September 8th 1809 contained several exceptionally interesting and colourful paragraphs. For example, His Majesty the King of Wurttemberg had passed a law "declaring every body out of his wits who presumed to talk freely or irreverently of his Royal person." And a Marylebone lamplighter had been sent to trial for wantonly drawing his burner across the breeches of a respectable young Scotsman named Alexander Campbell.

But for connoisseurs of the picturesque a letter sandwiched inconspicuously between the Ship News and the Price of Stocks must surely have provided the highlight of the day's news. It was from a Mr. William Munro, a schoolmaster of Thurso in Scotland, and was headed "The Mermaid Seen on the Coast of Caithness."

DEAR SIR—*About twelve years ago, when I was Parochial Schoolmaster at Reay, in the course of my walking on the shore of Sandside Bay, being a fine warm day in summer, I was induced to extend my walk towards Sandside Head, when my attention was arrested by the appearance of a figure resembling an unclothed human female, sitting upon a rock extending into the sea, and apparently in the action of combing its hair, which flowed around its shoulders, and was of a light brown colour. The forehead was round, the face plump, the cheeks ruddy, the eyes blue, the mouth and lips of a natural form, resembling those of a man; the teeth I could not discover, as the mouth was shut; the breasts and abdomen, the arms and fingers of the size of a full grown body of the human species; the fingers, from the action in which the hands were employed, did not appear to be webbed, but as to this I am not positive. It remained on the rock three or four minutes after I observed it, and was exercised during that period in combing its hair, which was long and thick, and of which it appeared proud, and then dropped into the sea, from whence it did not reappear to me. I had a distinct view of its features, being at no great distance on an eminence above the rock on which it was sitting, and the sun brightly shining.*

If the above narrative can in any degree be subservient towards establishing the existence of a phenomenon, hitherto almost incredible to naturalists, or to remove the scepticism of others, who are ready to dispute every thing which they cannot fully comprehend, you are welcome to it, from

Dear Sir

Your most obliged, and most humble servant,

(*Signed*) WM. MUNRO

Mr. Munro was not alone in his observation of this mysterious and romantic phenomenon. His letter to *The Times* had itself been prompted by the experience of a certain Miss Mackay and another girl, who had seen a creature of equally unusual physique bathing in a rough sea off the coast of Caithness earlier in the year. According to Miss Mackay, this creature had a face that was "round and plump and of a bright pink hue." Although not actually observed to have a comb, every now and then it would lift a slim white arm above the waves and toss back a mane of long green hair. Thus the two descriptions agreed together excellently and for a time there seemed every reason to hope that mermaids would be recognized as a valuable if unexpected addition to the marine fauna of Scotland.

Unfortunately, however, this romantic possibility was never to be realized. No further Scottish mermaids were seen, and in the absence of proof in the shape of a live specimen, or at least a corpse, naturalists preserved an aloof and dignified silence. Long before the end of the year the nine days' wonder was at an end, and Miss Mackay and Mr. Munro relapsed once more into the obscurity from which they had so briefly but gloriously emerged.

I have quoted this story at some length because it is a good example of the persistence into comparatively modern times of a legend that is nearly as old as the written records of man. There is not an age, and hardly a country in the world, whose folklore does not contain some reference to mermaids or to mermaid-like creatures. They have been alleged to appear in a hundred different places, ranging from the mist-covered shores of Norway and Newfoundland to the palm-studded islands of the tropic seas. Wherever they have been seen, the legends tell us that they have stirred up men's hearts to a strange mixture of emotions—to wonder and fear, ecstasy and irresistible desire.

The persistence of the mermaid legend, and the similarity of so many of the reports from independent sources in different areas, suggest that it is based on more than an idle fantasy of the human imagination. It seems certain, as I shall try to show later, that some real animal or, more likely, a number of different animals lie behind the legend in its various forms. But even when this is realized we do

4

not thereby gain a true insight into the subject. The natural history of mermaids cannot be understood, like that of mackerel or cod, by the methods of science alone. Even in reading Mr. Munro's letter we feel there is something misleading, not to say unchivalrous, about his purely clinical description of mermaid anatomy, and his insistence on the sexless and impersonal pronoun "it." Mermaids, even if their legend proves to be partly rooted in scientific fact, are too glamorous a theme to be treated in this way. I therefore make no excuse for prefacing my discussion of mermaid natural history with a *resumé* of their romantic mythological past.

A long path of association and evolving tradition lies between the mermaid's most ancient recorded ancestor and the green-haired, ripe-breasted girl of later times, with her comb and mirror, who beguiled unsuspecting sailors to destruction with her beauty and her seductive songs. We cannot even be sure of the line of her descent, so quickly do legends evolve, intermingle and change. But we can at least say, if we are to accept the general opinion of the mythologists, that the most ancient ancestor of all the mermaids was, in all probability, not a woman but a man: and yet not quite a man according to our modern conception, but an animal turned god, who rose from the Erythraean sea to teach mortals the values of civilization, and who stood in their eyes for the mysterious processes of healing and fertility and the life-giving power of the sun.

The story is told in a fragment of ancient history preserved for us by Berosus the Chaldean, a priest and astronomer of Babylon, who lived in the third century B.C. "The whole body of the animal," he says, "was like that of a fish; and had under a fish's head another head, and also feet below, like those of a man joined to its fish's tail. He was endowed with reason, and his voice and language were articulate and human. And he gave men an insight into letters and sciences, and every kind of art—into everything, in short, which could tend to soften manners and humanize mankind."

The name of this amiable creature was Oannes, the Babylonian fish god. He rose from the sea each morning, and at sunset plunged once more beneath the waves. Early pictures of Oannes represent

5

him as having human form, but with a fish's head worn as a cap. The skin of the fish hangs from his shoulders like a cloak, the tail reaching below his thighs, and sometimes as low as his ankles. His appearance in this costume makes a good approximation to the description of him given by Berosus, but is still only remotely suggestive of the form of his mermaid descendants.

In the next stage of Oannes' development, however, as preserved in ancient sculptures at Khorsabad and elsewhere, his figure has become greatly simplified, and he is shown with the upper parts of a man and the lower parts and tail of a fish. In this form he is usually identified with the Babylonian water god Ea, and sometimes with the Biblical Dagon. But scholars are cautious about the association with Dagon, feeling that although Oannes and Ea were undoubtedly "fishy," Dagon was more probably an Earth god particularly associated with corn. However this may be, it is now apparent that Oannes, with certain important differences, is approximating more nearly to the genus, if not the species, of the strange creature seen by Mr. Munro off the coast of Scotland. The most obvious and fundamental difference, of course, is that of his sex.

Of the feminine deities to whom the mermaid owes her ancestry the earliest is the Semitic moon goddess, Atergatis, or Derceto. She, like Oannes, was a fish deity, and was depicted at first with human extremities projecting from a fish-like cloak. But her form became altered also, so that in the words of Lucian, "she had the half of a woman, and from the thighs downwards a fish's tail." Glamorous as she was, she had an eye to practical matters, for she issued an edict that no one should go fishing without a license from herself. The dues from these licenses doubtless made a welcome addition to the funds administered by her high priests.

The reasons for the fish-like shape of Oannes and his feminine counterpart, Atergatis, provide a good example of the way myths change and grow. I mentioned earlier how Oannes was associated with the life-giving power of the sun. The idea of a sun god is as old as Palaeolithic man, maybe even older, and he is usually the most powerful and influential deity in primitive cosmologies. Oannes

6

himself was probably once exclusively a sun god, his quality as a civilizing power being a secondary attribute that grew up with the evolution of the world's first settled communities. But did not the sun rise at dawn from the sea, to fall into it once more at the close of the day? Then what more natural than that Oannes should be endowed with the shape of a man-fish, a supernatural power who came on land in the day time, spreading light and life, and plunged at night into the dark and mysterious wastes of the sea?

If these assumptions are correct, then Atergatis, the moon goddess, was endowed with her fish-like form because she was Oannes' feminine counterpart. Like him she rose from the surface of the ocean and returned to it at the end of her long journey across the night sky. She too, men argued, must be amphibious, part human, part fish; but less physically powerful and still more mysterious than Oannes, like woman herself. Thus the first fish goddess came into being, and her qualities spread and grew like a rumour or a legend. She took on in her person, under her different guises, the many attributes that men have always ascribed to women—beauty, vanity, pride, cruelty, seductiveness and unattainable love. Atergatis, and her many counterparts in other mythologies, was not, we may feel, an unlikely or unworthy ancestor of the mermaid of later times.

As a result of the prestige of the great fish gods and goddesses who were so widely worshipped by men before the Christian era, several lesser supernatural beings grew up in similar form. Thus Aphrodite, who is sometimes identified with Atergatis, and likewise rose from the sea, was served by two or more minor deities with human bodies and fishes' tails. These were the Tritons, who in addition to paying homage to Aphrodite, had certain powers of their own as sea gods, being able to calm the waves and rule the storm. The famous Sirens are also sometimes pictured in the form of mermaids, but this is not strictly accurate for they were first conceived as creatures with women's heads but bird-like, winged bodies. They nevertheless played an important part in the growth of the mermaid legend for they originated the idea of the fatal supernatural lover who lured mariners to their deaths, either by the beauty of their voices, which

7

caused the sailors to leap from their ships, or by casting the ship itself to destruction on the rocky shore. This power was later transferred to the mermaids, and so the Sirens, like the Tritons, can be regarded as one of the links which joined the fish gods and goddesses of pre-Christian mythology with the more recent developments of mermaid lore.

The earliest naturalist to deal with mermaids in any detail was Pliny the Elder, whose famous *Natural History* appeared in the first century A.D. Pliny was a man of forthright character, a cavalry officer and a writer of military history, whom one could never have suspected of undue credulity. Yet he not only believed in mermaids, being convinced that they were real creatures, but cited the most illustrious personages to support his opinion. Philemon Holland, Pliny's seventeenth century English translator, records his views on mermaids in such picturesque language and spelling that I cannot forbear quoting them in their original form. "And as for the Meremaids," he says, "it is no fabulous tale that goeth of them: for looke how painters draw them, so they are indeed: only their bodie is rough and skaled all over, even in those parts wherein they resemble a woman. For such a Meremaid was seene and beheld plainely upon a coast neere to the shore: and the inhabitants dwelling neere, heard it a farre off when it was a dying, to make pitteous mone, crying and chattering very heavily."

No one in seventeenth century England would have regarded these words of Pliny's as particularly surprising. They might have questioned the finer points of the description, but the existence of mermaids was as firmly established as the existence of shrimps. They were regularly seen off the coast of Britain, and travellers brought back tales of encounters with them from every corner of the seven seas. Two examples from this period will suffice, both reported by seamen of great knowledge and experience whom it would be difficult to accuse of an exaggerated gift for fantasy.

I have taken the first from the stolid, prosaic narrative of the voyages of Henry Hudson, published in London in 1625. Here is recorded, in the most matter-of-fact language, an incident which

8

occurred near Nova Zembla on one of Hudson's famous attempts to force the North West Passage:

This evening (June 15) one of our company, looking overboard, saw a mermaid, and, calling up some of the company to see her, one more of the crew came up, and by that time she was come close to the ship's side, looking earnestly on the men. A little after a sea came and overturned her. From the navel upward, her back and breasts were like a woman's, as they say that saw her; her body as big as one of us, her skin very white, and long hair hanging down behind, of colour black. In her going down they saw her tail, which was like the tail of a porpoise, speckled like a mackerel. Their names that saw her were Thomas Hilles and Robert Rayner.

The second mermaid report is taken from a description of the colony of Newfoundland by Sir Richard Whitbourne, a sea captain of Exmouth in Devon. Whitbourne had made numerous voyages to that country, and in 1620 he published his *Discourse and Discovery of New-found-land,* to give a picture of its amenities and to encourage new settlers. One of the more unusual episodes recorded reads as follows:

Now also I will not omit to relate something of a strange Creature, which I first saw there in the year 1610, in a morning early as I was standing by the River side, in the Harbour of St. Johns, which very swiftly came swimming towards me, looking cheerfully on my face, as it had been a woman: by the face, eyes, nose, mouth, chin, ears, neck and forehead, it seemed to be beautiful, and in those parts well proportioned having round about the head many blue streaks resembling hair, but certainly it was no hair. . . . It swam towards the place where a little before I landed, and it did often look back towards me; whereby I beheld the shoulders and back down to the middle to be so square, white and smooth as the back of a man; and from the middle to the hinder part it was pointing in proportion something like a broad hooked Arrow: how it was in the forepart

9

*from the neck and shoulders I could not well discern. . . . It came
shortly after to a Boat in the same Harbour (wherein one William
Hawkridge, then my servant, was) and did put both his hands upon
the side of the Boat, and did strive much to come in to him, and
divers then in the same Boat; whereat they were afraid, and one of
them struck it a full blow on the head, whereby it fell off from them.
. . . This (I suppose) was a Mermaid or Merman.*

Although we may dissent from this last opinion, it would be im-
possible to accuse such a sober and straightforward witness at Whitbourne of fraud or sensationalism. The episode obviously occurred
as it was described, and it was the identity, not the existence, of the
"strange Creature" that a later and more sophisticated generation
was to question. The mermaid, for the moment, continued to be
firmly entrenched in popular belief.

The eighteenth century, which prided itself on its worldliness,
cynicism, and good sense, was nevertheless as passionately addicted
to mermaids as the preceding age. One of the main protagonists of
their cause was François Valentijn, a Dutch colonial chaplain, who,
in his *Natural History of Amboina*, published in 1726, gives numerous accounts of their appearances in the East Indies. . . .

As the early eighteenth century wore on, naturalists found it in-
creasingly difficult to maintain even in their own minds a whole-
hearted belief in the mermaid's real existence. The famous author of
The Natural History of Norway, Erik Pontoppidan, dismisses a
great deal of what is said about them as mere idle talk, mentioning
particularly a merman who was reported to have spoken fluent
Danish to two Senators, and a mermaid who, it was alleged, had
foretold the birth of King Christian IV. "When such fictions are
mixed with the history of the Mermen," he grumbles, "and when
that is represented as a prophet and an orator; when they give the
Mermaid a melodious voice, and tell us that she is a fine singer; one
need not wonder that so few people of sense will give credit to such
absurdities; or that they even doubt the existence of such a creature."
Yet even Pontoppidan cannot bring himself to reject the mermaid

altogether, for he follows his reservations with eight folio pages devoted to the "true" natural history of the genus.

It would be possible to multiply the tales of mermaids seen, or reported seen, almost indefinitely. Many of these were obviously fictitious, and contained every element from the higher flights of alcoholic fancy down to plain bare-faced lying. For instance, there was the story of the exceptionally beautiful mermaid captured in the early eighteenth century by Manx fishermen and kept for several days in a house in the village before being returned to her native element. The only comment made by this creature as she rejoined her own people in the surf—a comment, moreover, that was distinctly heard by the fishermen standing on the shore to watch—was that human beings were so exceedingly ignorant that they threw away the water in which they had boiled eggs. Other stories, like those recorded by Hudson, Whitbourne, Valentijn and Pontoppidan, seem undoubtedly to have had a substratum of fact, while others again are borderline cases. One of these last is the legend of the man-fish who is said to have conducted Indian tribes from Asia to North America, and whose anatomy seems to belong partly to zoology and partly to myth. Another is the story of the merman seen by several persons on the coast of Martinique who was approached so closely that it was seen to wipe its hands across its face and actually heard to blow its nose.

I have unfortunately no space here to elaborate these promising themes. There is, however, one further aspect of mermaid lore that must be touched upon before we proceed to the less frivolous zoological aspects of the subject. Despite the growing momentum of scientific knowledge, a widespread belief in mermaids, which contained wonder but no scepticism, persisted among certain classes of the community until well into the reign of Queen Victoria. We have already seen the serious approach to the subject made by Mr. Munro and sanctioned by the august authority of *The Times*. By the middle of the century little change had occurred in this attitude except among the cognoscenti, and enterprising showmen had decided that the time was now ripe to take advantage of it. Hence the sudden

11

appearance in certain rather dubious quarters of nineteenth century London of "stuffed mermaids," which it was alleged had been caught along a variety of mysterious and romantic shores somewhere east of Suez and brought to London for the delectation of the public.

Francis Buckland in his *Curiosities of Natural History*, published between 1858 and 1866, records several instances of the display of these oddities. The most famous was that shown in London at the Egyptian Hall in the 1830's, which was sold to two Italian brothers for 40,000 dollars and ended up as the subject of an embittered legal wrangle. Buckland himself gives a description of another stuffed mermaid that was established in 1858 in the back parlour of the White Hart at Spitalfields. It was between three and four feet long and was obligingly removed by the publican from its glass case so that Buckland could examine it. According to his description it was of the regulation mermaid pattern, half fish and half "human," with hideous parchment-like ears standing well forward, a snub nose, the forehead wrinkled into a frown, and the lips curled into a ghastly grin. To establish its quasi-human nature beyond a doubt the lower jaw was equipped with an unmistakable human incisor tooth. A close examination of this repellent but fascinating object revealed that the upper part of its body consisted of the head, trunk and arms of a monkey, while the lower half, to which it was most carefully stitched, consisted of the skin of a fish which Buckland unromantically conjectured to be hake.

This particular composite mermaid had been made by an enterprising bird-stuffer in the West End, but the main centre of the art was probably Japan. According to Andrew Steinmetz's fascinating book *Japan and Her People*, published in 1859, Japanese fishermen found the traffic in artificial mermaids an invaluable means of supplementing their income. The system was briefly this. First the mermaid itself was artfully manufactured out of a monkey and a fish. The fisherman would then give out that the creature had been taken alive in his nets, but had shortly afterwards died. Profit accrued from two sources. First there was the money paid by the curious to inspect the body. The fisherman would then announce that shortly before the mermaid expired she had predicted a fatal epidemic from which the only protection would be the wearing of her own picture as a charm. Naturally the fisherman had a plentiful supply of such pictures on hand, and there can have been few of his superstitious countrymen who dared to tempt providence by going away without one.

Europe saw many of these Japanese mermaids during the nineteenth century, mostly as catchpennies in public exhibitions. The great American showman, P. T. Barnum, was particularly adept at exploiting them in his sideshows and fun fairs—a process he used to describe with obvious relish in a lecture aptly entitled "Humbug." Other Japanese mermaids were to be found in the private collections of naturalists and curio hunters. . . . Even today there is, I am told, a distinguished Cambridge professor who possesses an admirably preserved specimen, and has spent many agreeable hours in X-raying its interior.

I think I have now said enough to show the extraordinary vitality of the mermaid legend, which has caused it to persist for nearly 3,000 years and to be carried to every country in the world. It only remains to enquire why this should have been. In the first place there was the association of mermaids with the all-powerful sun god of early pagan religion, which undoubtedly gave the legend its original impetus. Secondly, there was the additional significance it acquired in course of time by association with the concept of ideal, but fatal, love embodied in the person of a remote and mysterious feminine being who could never be finally possessed by a living man. This concept appealed to the basic sexual and we may perhaps dare to add, even in a psychological age, spiritual instincts of mankind. The mermaid was the princess of medieval chivalry, the nineteenth century romantic's *idée fixe,* and the modern *femme fatale* rolled into one. But even when these emotional factors are taken into account they cannot explain many of the more prosaic and factual mermaid reports that have appeared from time to time. In some, at least of these, it seems certain that a real animal was involved, which became "transformed" into a mermaid by the expectant attention of the superstitious mariners who witnessed it.

It is perhaps unfortunate that the animal that has been cast most often in the role of mermaid goes by the unromantic popular name of sea-cow. For once, however, science has been kinder and more romantic and termed the order to which these real-life mermaids belong the Sirenia, or sirens. Until just over a hundred years ago this order of the animal kingdom was represented by three different genera, but the largest and most extraordinary of them, *Rhytina stelleri*, or Steller's sea-cow, is now extinct and will be dealt with later. It is not in any case likely that *Rhytina* could ever have been mistaken for a mermaid, except a very robust one, for it grew regularly to a length of twenty-five feet or more. The honour is therefore left to its smaller surviving relatives, the manatee and the dugong.

Both these creatures come from the tropics, the manatee frequenting the estuaries and big rivers of the African and American Atlantic coasts, the dugong being found in the Indian Ocean and along the shores of Australia and the East Indies. Their charm, at least as regards their appearance, is limited, but the details of their anatomy do bear some relation to that traditionally ascribed to mermaids. For instance their bodies are only slightly larger than a human being's, and unlike most mammals they have their breasts, or mammae, situated well forward on the trunk near the flipper-like forelimbs. There are no rear limbs at all and the body tapers to a rounded, and horizontally flattened tail. But despite these peculiarities, they are a very poor substitute for the seductive sea maidens of mythology. The thick and protruding upper lip is cleft in the middle for greater ease in cropping vegetation, and while the face of the manatee is almost hairless, the dugong is decidedly whiskered. The expression of both creatures, if harmless, is a trifle vacant, and one is additionally disconcerted to learn that their nearest animal relations are probably the elephant and the tapir. As Henry Lee, of the Brighton Aquarium, remarks, distance must lend enchantment to the view, for it would be a very impressionable and imaginative sailor who, even after many weeks at sea without the company of women, could be

14

allured by the charms of a bristly-muzzled dugong, or mistake the snorting of a wallowing manatee for the love song of a mermaid.

But in addition to the shape of the manatees and dugongs, there are other factors that confirm their association with the mermaid legend. The dugong especially is said to suckle its young with the upper part of its body projecting from the water, holding the baby dugong to its breast with one flipper. If disturbed, the animal will plunge beneath the surface, often flicking its tail in the air as it does so. The young have also been heard to utter the doleful whimpering cries associated with some of the reports.

Many of the mermaid stories from the coasts of Africa and Asia have almost certainly been inspired by a distant or indistinct view of a dugong or manatee in the act of submerging; but it is obvious that such an explanation will not hold good for the vision vouchsafed to Mr. Munro off the coast of Caithness, for the range of the Sirenia is entirely confined to the tropic coasts. The animal most likely to account for the various appearances of mermaids in colder latitudes is therefore probably one of the world's thirty species of seals.

There are three different families of seals comprised in the Pinnipedia, or "fin feet," as this sub-order is scientifically termed. The Otariidae, or eared seals, and the Odobaenidae, or walruses, may on occasion have been responsible for mermaid reports—in fact the man-fish of the North American Indians was in my opinion almost certainly a walrus; but Mr. Munro's mermaid and others reported from British waters were probably members of the third family, the Phocidae, or true seals. Two British members of this group are well known. The common seal, *Phoca vitulina,* is common in Shetland and Orkney, and down the east coast of Britain as far as the Wash. It is also found on the west coast, but here it is largely replaced by the second British species, the Atlantic seal, *Halichoerus grypus.*

Not everyone will agree that seals could in any circumstances be mistaken for mermaids, and certainly when they are seen at close quarters in a zoo or under similar controlled conditions, the theory is a little difficult to swallow. But in a storm-tossed sea off the Scottish coast, or seen at a distance from a cliff top, the likeness is not really so very far fetched. The body of the phocid seal tapers to a point in the same way as that of the Sirenia, and their hind limbs are permanently extended backwards, so that the rear part of the trunk strongly resembles the typical mermaid tail. Moreover, the plump, rounded, expressive face of the seal, its soft, intelligent eyes, and handlike fore-flippers give it a most human character, which is still further emphasized when, as often occurs, it poises itself in the water with only the upper part of its body protruding.

To prove this likeness, Henry Lee cites an occasion when he was sailing off the mouth of the river Maas near the Hook of Holland and a seal appeared in the attitude described above. It watched the yacht go by with the greatest curiosity, then dived and took up its station once more in the waters ahead. It repeated the process three times and could so easily have been mistaken for a human form that one of the occupants of the yacht thought it was a boy who had swum off from the shore on a begging expedition. Anyone who has watched the behaviour of seals when their interest and curiosity, but not their fear, has been aroused, will know that this is by no means an unlikely incident.

The natural history of mermaids, therefore, seems in many of its aspects to be safely comprised within the natural history of sea cows and seals. No longer, with Philip Gosse, can we entertain the wistful hope "that green-haired maidens with oary tails lurk in the ocean caves, and keep mirrors and combs upon their rocky shelves." But as I said at the beginning of this chapter, the natural history of mermaids cannot be understood by the methods of natural science alone. These hauntingly beautiful goddesses of the sea, full of mystery and danger, were surely conjured from the chaos of the waters in answer to some primal human need. Their genus and species may not be carefully docketed in the *Nomenclator Zoologicus*, but their reality in terms of poetic truth is firmly established in the impassioned imagination of men.

John Reid and
the Mermaid

ELIZABETH SHEPPARD JONES

JOHN REID was a shipmaster who owned a large sloop with which he traded between Holland and the northern ports of Scotland. He was lucky in business and grew wealthy as the years went by. He should have been a happy man but, in fact, he was one of the unhappiest men alive because he was in love with the beautiful Helen Stuart who was not in love with him. She was many years younger than he, and after they had first met, he thought of her all day and dreamed of her all night. She only vaguely remembered a pleasant, good-humoured

17

man, broad-shouldered and with skin tanned to a deep bronze.

The months passed and John Reid still thought of Helen Stuart. Towards the end of April, he returned from one of his trips, determined to have another glimpse of the lady. He knew that on May-Day she would be out with her companions, gathering May-dew, so he rose early that day and wandered along the seashore. The stars disappeared one by one, and the sun rose and flung a path of flame across the water. But John Reid did not stop to admire the beauty of the dawn, he could think only of Helen Stuart.

As he clambered over the rocks, he heard the low notes of a song. He looked around him to see if a fisherman in a boat was passing by or a shepherd whistling on the hillside, but he could only see a huge bull seal that had raised its head above the waves as if it, too, were listening to the music. When John reached the other side of the rocks, he saw the singer. It was a young girl sitting half on a rock, half in the water. Her long hair fell thickly on her creamy shoulders and, as she pulled herself up on to the rock, the sun shone on her lower half with such brightness that the sailor had to shield his eyes for a moment.

"The sun glitters thus on fish that are freshly caught," murmured John to himself. "Of course—she is a mermaid! It is the scales of her tail that shine so brightly."

He would have pretended he had not seen her and gone on his way, had he not suddenly remembered that mermaids have strange powers. Perhaps this one could help to make Helen Stuart love him.

He crept in and out of the rocks until he was behind her. She turned round, and the last note of her song changed to a shriek of alarm. She tried to fling herself into the water, but John Reid had locked his brawny arms firmly round her fishy waist. She struggled with the strength of a whale. John's muscles quivered with the strain of holding her and, had not the thought of Helen Stuart kept him firm, he would have let go. The mermaid's struggles became fainter and fainter until he was able to drag her farther up the beach.

"Man, what do you want with me?" she asked weakly in a voice which, though as sweet as the song of a bird, was sea-cold like the bottom of the ocean.

"Three wishes," said John Reid, remembering what was supposed to be the correct answer to such a question.

"Speak on," said the mermaid.

"My father, a sailor like myself," said John, "was drowned many years ago. My first wish is that neither I, nor any of my friends, shall be drowned at sea. My second wish is that I shall continue to prosper as I have done recently. My third wish is that Helen Stuart, whom I love, shall, in turn, love me."

"Quit, and have," replied the mermaid.

John Reid released his hold on her. Pressing her tail against a rock until it curled to her waist, she shot into the sea like an uncoiled spring. A slight ripple splashed against the beach. All trace of the mermaid had vanished. John wiped his brow and, with hope in his heart, climbed up the hill, at the top of which he expected to find Helen. And there she was, sitting with a friend on the grass, near a spot appropriately known as Lover's Leap. Fortune had already begun to favour the sailor.

"Fancy seeing you here, John Reid!" exclaimed Helen's companion. "Helen has been telling us of a dream she had last night. She dreamt she was gathering May-dew, but the grass and bushes were dry and she had collected only a few drops when she heard someone singing near the rocks on the shore. Then she saw you asleep on the beach and the singer, a lovely lady, by your side. Helen was afraid you would not wake before the tide covered you, but suddenly you were standing beside her, and began to help her shake the bushes for dew. She looked for the singing lady and saw her far out on the sea, floating on the waves like a white seagull. As she wondered at this, she heard the drops of water which you had shaken down, tinkling against the bottom of her bucket. And, just imagine, John Reid, the drops had turned into pieces of pure gold!"

"That is quite true," said Helen. "But the strangest part of it all is that, as we passed up the slope this morning, I heard among the rocks on the beach the same song which I heard in my dream. I hope now you are going to fill our buckets with gold."

She laughed and John laughed, too.

"You may have heard the magic music," he said, "but I have seen and talked with the singer. She is a mermaid."

"Seen and talked with the mermaid!" cried Helen's friend. "Heaven forbid! The last time she appeared was a few days before that terrible storm in which you lost your father. Take care not to repeat her words, for they thrive ill who carry tales from the other world to this."

"Don't worry," replied John. "I am the mermaid's master; I had the better of her. I have no need to be afraid."

And he went on to tell his story. He told them only two of his three wishes, but there was a gleam in Helen's eyes that suggested she guessed the nature of the third. She listened to him in wonder and admiration and, when she realized the danger he had been in, her heart filled with love for him. They walked home together, Helen leaning on the sailor's arm for support and protection. And by next May-Day they were man and wife.

John O'Glin

MR. and MRS. S. C. HALL

Tired of looking over the blue waters for the boat he had expected since morning, John lay down beneath the shadow of a rock and fell asleep. Now the place he had chosen to repose in was for all the world like a basket; there was the high rock above him, and a ledge of rock all round, so that where he lay might be called a sandy cradle. There he slumbered as snug as an egg in a thrush's nest, and he might have slept about two hours when he heard singing.

He never heard the like before: the words were queerer than

the music—for John was a fine scholar and had a quarter's Latin to say nothing of six months' dancing; so that he could flog the world at single or double-handed reel, and split many a door with the strength of his hornpipe.

"Blessed father," he says, "to my own knowledge it's neyther Latin nor Hebrew they're at, nor any other livin' language." So, 'cute enough, he dragged himself up to the edge of the ledge of the rock that overlooked the wide ocean, and what should he see but about twenty fine well-grown men and women dancing a solemn sort of dance on the sands while they sung their unnatural song, and the ladies' hair was twisted and twined round and round their heads.

Well, John grew the less fearful the longer he looked; and at last his attention was drawn off the strangers by a great heap of skins that were piled together on the strand close beside him. They were seal skins, shining all of them like satin, though some were black, and more of them grey; but at the very top of the pile right under his hand was the most curious of them all—snowy and silver white. Soothering it down with his hand, he thought no down of the young wild swan was ever half so smooth, and when he was thinking and judging what it would fetch in Newport, or maybe Galway, there was a screech among the dancers and singers.

Before poor John had time to return the skin, all of them came hurrying toward where he lay. Believing they were sea pirates, or some new-fashioned revenue officers, he crept into the sand, dragging the silver-coloured skin with him. Well, nothing could equal the 'ullabaloo and "shindy" kicked up all about where he lay—such talking and screaming and bellowing, and at last he heard another awful roar, and then all was still, except a sort of snuffling and snorting in the sand. When that had been over some time, he drew himself cautiously up on his elbows, and after securing the skin in his bosom he moved on, and on, until at last he rested his chin upon the very top of the ledge, and casting his eye along the line of coast, not a sight or a sign of any living thing did he see but a great fat seal walloping as fast as ever it could into the ocean.

Well, he shook himself, and stood up; when, just round the corner of the rock, he heard the low wailing voice of a young girl, soft, and low, and full of sorrow. To spring over was the work of a single minute; and, sure enough, sitting there was as lovely a young lady as John ever looked on. She had a loose sort of dress, drawn in at her throat with a gold string, and he saw at once that she was one of the outlandish people who had disappeared.

"Avourneen das! my lady," says John, making his best bow, "and what ails you, darling stranger?" Well, she only looked askew at him, and John O'Glin thought she didn't sigh so bitterly as she had done at first; and he came a little nearer, and "Cushla ma Chree, beauty of the waters," he says, "I'm sorry for your trouble."

So she turns round her little face to him, and her eyes were as dark as the best black turf, and as round as a periwinkle.

"Creature," she says, "do you speak Hebrew?"

"I'd speak anything," he answers, "to speak with you."

"Then," she says again, "have you seen my skin?"

"Yes, darling," he says in reply, looking at her with every eye in his head.

"Where, where is it?" she cries, jumping up and clasping her two little hands together, and dropping on her knees before John.

"Where is it?" he repeats, raising her gently up. "Why on yourself, to be sure, as white and as clear as the foam on a wave in June."

"Oh, it's the other skin I want," she cries bursting into tears.

"Shall I skin myself and give it you, to please you, my lady?" he replies. "I will, and welcome, if it will do you any good, sooner than have you bawling and roaring this way," he says.

"What a funny creature you are!" she answers laughing up in his face, "but you're not a seal," she says, "and so your skin would do me no good."

"Whew!" thought John O'Glin; "whew! now all the blossom is out on the maybush; now my eyes are opened," for he knew the sense of what he had seen.

"I'll tell you what it is," said the poor fellow, for it never took him any time at all to fall in love. "Don't bother any more about your bit of a skin, but take me instead—that is," he said, and he changed

23

colour at the bare thought of it, "that is, unless you're married in your own country."

And as all their discourse went on in Hebrew and Latin, which John had not a perfect knowledge of, he found it hard to make her understand at first, though she was quick enough too; and she said she was not married, but might have been, only she had no mind to the seal who was her father's prime minister but that she had always made up her mind to marry none but a prince. "And are you a king's son?" she says.

"More than that," says John, "I've the blood in my veins of twenty kings—and what's better than that, Irish kings."

"And have you a palace to take me to?" she says, "and a golden girdle to give me?"

Now this, John thought, was mighty mean of her; but he looked in her eyes and forgot it. "Our love," he says, "pulse of my beating heart, will build its own palace; and this girdle," and he falls on his knees by her side, and throws his arm around her waist, "is better than a girdle of gold!"

Well, to be sure there was no boy in Mayo had better right to know how to make love than John O'Glin, for no one ever had more practice; and the upshot of it was, that (never, you may be sure, letting on to her about the sealskin) he carried her home; and that same night after he had hid the skin in the thatch, he went to the priest—and he told him a good part of the truth; and when he showed his reverence how she had fine gold rings and chains, and as much cut coral as would make a reef, the priest did not look to hear any more, but tied them at once.

Time passed on gaily with John O'Glin, his wife helped him wonderful at the fishing—there wasn't a fin could come within half a mile of her that she wouldn't catch—ay, and bring to shore too; but she'd never wait to dress anything for herself, only eat it raw; and this certainly gave him a great deal of uneasiness. She'd eat six herrings, live enough to go down her throat of themselves without hardly drawing her breath, and spoil the market of cod or salmon, by biting off the tails. When John would speak to her about it, why she'd cry and want to go back to her father, and go poking about after the skin, which she'd never mention at any other time, so John thought it would be best to let her have her own way, for when she had, it's nursing the children, and singing, and fishing she'd be all day long.

They had three little children, and John had full and plenty for them all and was a sober steady man, well to do; and there were no prettier children in all the barony than the "Seal-woman's"; with such lovely hair and round blinking eyes, that set the head swimming in no time; and they had sweet voices, and kind hearts that would share the last bit they had in the world with any one that knew what it was to be hungry; and, the Lord knows, it isn't in Mayo their hearts would stiffen for want of practice.

Still John was often uneasy about his wife. More than once, when she went with him to the shore, he'd seen one or two seals walloping nearer than he liked; and once, when he took up his gun to fire at a great bottle-nosed one that was asleep on the sandbank, she made him swear never to do so: "For who knows," she says, "but it's one of my relations you'd be murdering?" And sometimes she'd sit melancholy-like, watching the waves, and tears would roll down her little cheeks; but John would soon kiss them away.

Poor fellow! much as he loved her, he knew she was a sly little devil; for when he'd be lamenting latterly how 'cute the fish were grown, or anything that way, she'd come up and sit down by him, and lay her soft round cheek close to his, and take his hand between hers, and say, "Ah, John darlin' if you'd only find my skin for me that I lost when I found you, see the beautiful fish I'd bring you from the bottom of the sea, and the fine things. Oh, John, it's you then could drive a carriage through Newport, if there were but roads to drive on."

Yet he was heart-proof against her soft, deludering, soothering ways when she'd talk of the skin—and she never got any good of him about it—at all! But there's no end to female wit; they'll sit putting that and that together, and looking as soft and as fair-faced all the while as if they had no more care than a blind piper's dog, that has nothing to do but to catch the halfpence.

"I may as well give up watching her," said John to himself; "for even if she did find it, she'd never leave the children." So he gave her a parting kiss, and set off to the fair of Castlebar. He was away four days and his mind reproached him on his way home for leaving her so long; for he was very tender about her, seeing that though she was only a seal's daughter, that seal was a king. He made up his mind he'd never quit her so long again.

But when he came home to the door, it did not fly open, as it used, and show him his pretty wife, his little children, and a sparkling turf fire—he had to knock at his own door!

"Push it in, daddy," cried out the eldest boy, "mammy shut it after her, and we're weak with the hunger." So John did as his child told him, and his heart fainted, and he staggered into the room, and then up the ladder to the thatch—IT WAS GONE!—and John sat down, and his children climbed about him, and they all wept bitterly.

"Oh, daddy, why weren't you back the second day, as you said you'd be?" said one. "Mammy bade us kiss you and love you, and that she'd come back if she'd be let; but she found something in the thatch that took her away."

"She'll never come back, darlings, till we're all in our graves," said poor John. "She'll never come back under ninety years; and where will we all be then? She was ten years my delight and ten years my joy, and she was the best of mothers to ye all! but she's gone—she's gone for ever! Oh, how could you leave me, and I so fond of ye? Maybe I should have burnt the skin, only for the knowledge that if I did, I would shorten her days on earth, and her soul would have to begin over again as a baby seal, and I couldn't do what would be all as one as murder."

So poor John lamented, and betook himself and the three children to the shore, and would wail and cry, but he never saw her after; and the children grew up very sharp indeed at the learning, and excelled in the languages, beating priest, minister, and schoolmaster—particularly at the Hebrew. More than once, though John never saw her, he heard his wife singing the songs they often sung together, right under the water; and he'd sing in answer, and then there'd be a sighing and sobbing. Oh! it was very hard upon John, for he never married again, though he knew he'd never live till her time was up to come again upon the earth even for twelve hours; but he was a fine moral man all the latter part of his life.

~~~~~ ❀ ~~~~~

Sea-Trows

THOMAS KEIGHTLEY

WITH RESPECT to the Sea-Trows, it is the belief of the Shetlanders that they inhabited a region of their own at the bottom of the sea. They here respire a peculiar atmosphere, and live in habitations constructed of the choicest submarine productions. When they visit the upper world on occasions of business or curiosity, they are obliged to enter the skin of some animal capable of respiring in the water. One of the shapes they assume is that of what is commonly called a merman or mermaid, human from the waist upwards, terminating below in the tail of a fish. But their favorite vehicle is the skin of the larger seal or Haafe fish, for as this animal is amphibious they can land on some rock, and there cast off their sea-dress and assume their own shape, and amuse themselves as they will in the upper world. They must, however, take especial care of their skins, as each has but one, and if that should be lost, the owner can never re-descend, but must become an inhabitant of the supramarine world.

Scylla
and Charybdis

BARBARA LEONIE PICARD

THAT VERY DAY they set out once more on the long voyage home; and the enchantress Circe, who in the end had proved so good a friend to them, stood on the sand and watched the ship out of sight, speeded on its way by a fresh breeze which she herself had called up.

Once at sea, Odysseus thought fit to warn his men about the Sirens whose isle they soon would pass. But because he ever wished to know all that there was to know, he bade his comrades, when they neared the isle bind him with strong ropes to the mast and resist all pleading to untie him; so that he might hear the song the Sirens sang. He took a round ball of beeswax, and cutting off pieces with his sword, he kneaded them with his fingers; until, warmed by the sunshine and his hands, the wax grew soft. Then with it he stopped the ears of all his men, so that they might hear nothing. Three of them then tied him to the mast with strong ropes tightly knotted. A short distance on, the wind died down, the men had to take to their oars; and thus they approached the Sirens' isle.

The two Sirens perched upon their little islet, which was like a flowery meadow whereon grew purple irises, many-hued anemones, and the little yellow crocus. But round the margin of the island, where the sea washed the shore, was a wide wreath of bones, whitened by the sun. The Sirens had the bodies of great feathered birds; wide wings and feet with claws; but their heads as the heads of women, beautiful and kindly smiling, with long, flowing hair. And their voices were the sweetest sound in all the world. "Come, brave Odysseus, noblest of the Greeks," they said, "come to us and listen to our song. All men who go by our island pause to listen to our lay, and it gives them strength and courage and wisdom for all time. Only a madman or a fool would not stay for our singing, for we know and can sing of everything that has happened since the world began."

When Odysseus heard their voices he forgot all else, and knew only that he must stay and listen to their song. And he signed to his men with nods and frowns to loose him from his bonds, and struggled to free himself; yet they took no notice of his signs, for he had bidden them heed him not. But when his struggles grew too violent, Eurylochus feared that the ropes might break, and jumping up, he went to Odysseus and tightened the bonds.

And when at last the ship had passed the Sirens and their singing could no longer be heard, Odysseus's men took the wax from their ears and unbound him.

But before he had time to answer their questions as to what song the Sirens sang and how sweet their voices were, a great noise was heard as of a mighty fountain, and Odysseus knew that they were near Charybdis. At once his men ceased rowing and stared before them in terror at the two rocks on either side of the narrow strait, one high and misty and the other low with a fig tree growing on it.

Odysseus went among them with words of encouragement and comfort. "My friends, we have been in many perils together, but we have lived through them all. And indeed, this new danger cannot be worse than the Cyclops in his cave; and yet I brought you out alive from that monster's den. Be guided by me now and we may be saved. Row as you have never rowed before, and look not aside from your oars." Then to the helmsman he spoke, "Steer clear of the churning and thundering around the lower of the rocks, and keep close in beside the tall cliff." But he did not tell them of Scylla in her cave halfway up the rock, lest fear should take the strength from their arms and make them feeble.

In the hope that he might lop off one of Scylla's heads, Odysseus put on his helmet and took up his shield and sword and stood waiting on the deck, watching carefully the surface of the taller rock. It was indeed a high cliff, with its summit hidden in the mist, and its sides as smooth and polished as a silver mirror. But though he strained his eyes with looking, Odysseus could catch no sight of Scylla, nor hear her yapping like a dog.

Opposite no farther than a man could shoot an arrow, stood the low flat rock beneath which Charybdis dwelt. Upon it the great fig tree stretched out its branches, thick with glossy leaves and green, unripe fruit, while below, when Charybdis sucked down the water, could be seen the very bottom of the sea; and when she spouted it forth again, it was like a great pot boiling over on a flaming fire, with spray and steam and swirling waters and a mighty hissing.

The nearer the ship came, the more awful grew the sound; and as they rowed into the narrow strait, Odysseus turned to see the foaming whirlpool and relaxed his watch for Scylla. Instantly she leaned out from her cave halfway up the smooth rock and pounced upon rowers with each of her six heads. At their cries Odysseus turned, his sword ready, but it was even then too late and he could not reach the monster as she dangled the unhappy men above the ship. Her six hideous heads had each three rows of teeth, struggle as they might, her poor victims could not escape; and she devoured them at the opening of her cave, while they called for help.

With all their might Odysseus's men rowed on, till at last they were safely past the rocks and out into the open sea.

But though they had won through the perils of Scylla and Charybdis with no more than the loss of six men, there lay before them that far greater danger of which both Teiresias and Circe had warned Odysseus: the cattle of the sun-god on the island of Thrinacia.

They sighted the island towards evening, and the thought of land was welcome indeed to the tired men. The first man to see it raised a shout, and all eyes looked eagerly to where he pointed. "We are fortunate at last, and tonight we shall eat and sleep on land once more, away from the endless rolling of the sea."

But even before they reached the island they heard the lowing of cattle and the bleating of sheep; and as they came nearer they could plainly see the herds and flocks grazing on the grassy meadows, fine beasts of mighty size and noble appearance, fit for the ownership of an immortal god, their sleek white hides and woolly fleeces gilded by the setting sun.

"It is the island of Thrinacia," said Odysseus, "and those beasts are the cattle and sheep of Helios, who is the sun-god. Both Teiresias the prophet and Circe the enchantress warned me with strict and earnest words that we should take care to harm not the herds of the Sun if we would ever see our homes again. To avert the danger, let us not set foot upon the island. Row on, good men, and let us bear a small discomfort to avoid a greater grief."

But they protested at his words, and called to him how tired they were, how weary of the sea; and reminded him that for hours they had been rowing, while he, their leader, had been idle, watching the blue water. He answered them without anger, for he knew they spoke the truth; but for all his compassion he would not let them land, but bade them row on; if need be, all through the night.

Then Eurylochus spoke bitterly. "Because you are stronger than we are, Odysseus, and because your heart is iron, you will not grant us rest and the sweet relief of sleep upon a shore. Instead you order us to row on into the darkness, and who knows that we shall not be rowing on into a tempest which will wreck our ship and drown us every one, and all because you ordered it. Just for tonight let us cook our supper on the shore and sleep upon the sand, and in the morning we will sail with the first light of day."

The men called out in agreement. "Yes, Odysseus, let us rest tonight. We will sail at dawn and no harm can come of it."

So Odysseus sighed and gave way to their entreaties. But before they set foot upon the land, he made them swear an oath to keep away from the sacred sheep and cattle on the isle, and be content with the provisions with which Circe had stocked their ship.

They moored the ship in a little harbour near a spring, and built fires upon the shore to cook their food, and unsealed a jar of rich crimson wine, made from the grapes of Aeaea. And when they had eaten and drunk, they lay down upon the sand and slept, wrapped in their warm cloaks. But in the night a tempest rose and the wind blew wildly from the south, and in the morning it had not dropped and they could not sail. They dragged the ship up on to the beach and hid her in a cave; and once more Odysseus warned his men against harming the cattle which grazed peacefully in the pasture-lands near the shore, and he gave orders that of the food which remained to them, no man was to have more than his fair daily share.

So long as there was food left they never questioned the wisdom of his warning; for there were none of them that doubted that it would be unwise to meddle with the property of an immortal god. But the south wind blew boisterously for a month, and long before the thirty days were over, the food was gone; and there was no wild game upon the island.

They drank cold water from the spring to calm their hunger; they dug up to eat, from deep below the sand, the bulbs of the sweet-scented white lilies which grew above the water's edge; and searched among the rocks for crabs. With hooks of bent wire they fished, wading out from the shore; but rarely caught a fish of any size. They tore limpets from the rocks, and endlessly they turned over stones upon the beach, seeking for the little sea-creatures underneath. And once in a while a well-aimed stone would kill a seabird, and it would fall upon the shore. And ever in the ears of the starving men was the lowing of sleek cattle and the bleating of fat sheep; and ever before their eyes were the glossy white oxen and the snowy-fleeced sheep of Helios the sun-god.

When it was the twentieth day since they had landed on Thrinacia, while Odysseus, weakened by starvation, slept in a place that was sheltered from the ceaseless wind, Eurylochus spoke to his companions. "Whatever way death comes to us, it comes unwelcomed, but I at least would prefer not to die of hunger. What say you, friends, why do we not drive off a few of the fattest of those cows and kill them while Odysseus sleeps? If the gods are angry with us afterwards, and wreck our ship, then no doubt we shall be drowned. But is it not better to die quickly in the sea, than slowly to starve with so much good meat grazing on every side?"

And because the men were hungry, and saw no other way to save their lives, they agreed with Eurylochus, and at once they went and drove off three or four of the finest of the cattle and killed and flayed them on the beach. They built a huge fire, and cutting up the meat, turned it on spits before the blaze; and never had they waited so longingly for a meal to cook.

Odysseus awoke to smell the roasting meat, and instantly he knew what had been done. With horror in his heart he ran back to the shore, and bitterly he blamed his men for their rash disobedience. But it was too late for help, and no one could undo the deed. The sacred cattle had been killed and cooked, and such a crime it was certain Helios would never overlook.

"The immortal gods will avenge this sacrilege," said Odysseus, "there will be no escape for us."

And truly, in that moment the anger of the gods was shown in wondrous signs. A lowing as of cattle came from the meat upon the spits and the flayed hides moved upon the sands. But for all these portents Odysseus's men could not hold back from the meat, but fell upon it and ate eagerly.

For six days longer they remained on Thrinacia, and on the seventh day the wind dropped and veered, and at once they dragged the ship down to the water's edge, and unfurling the sail, put out to sea, leaving behind them the island where they had spent so many bitter days, and the herds which were soon to bring disaster on them.

When the island was out of sight and no other land had appeared on the horizon, a black cloud moved across the sun and a heavy shadow lay over the sea and a wild wind came howling from the west. The wind broke the forestays of the mast, so that the mast fell into the ship, killing the helmsman as it fell. A flash of lightning struck the ship asunder, and Odysseus's men were hurled into the waves; and not one of them was saved.

But Odysseus clung to the wrecked ship until the sea battered her apart, breaking away the sides and tearing off the mast by the keel. Then lashing the keel and the mast together with the oxhide backstay, Odysseus held to them, driven over the waves by the rushing wind.

After a time the west wind died down, and the south wind arose, blowing Odysseus back across the sea towards the straits where dwelt Scylla and Charybdis.

At dawn, he saw that he was close by the vortex of Charybdis, and try as he might with all his strength, he could not keep the mast and keel from being sucked down by the hidden monster.

As they vanished into the whirlpool, Odysseus jumped clear and clutched hold of the trunk of the fig tree growing from the rock. He held on to it with hands and legs, unable to climb up into its branches for they hung too high above his head, and unable to gain a firmer foothold for the rock was too low down. There he clung, like a bat upon a wall, until Charybdis spouted forth the mast and keel. Then he let himself drop back into the water, and clambering once more upon these precious spars, rowed with his hands in frantic haste, away from the dread rock where Charybdis lurked, before she should gulp down another draught of sea.

And after that, for nine days Odysseus clung to the mast and keel, borne here and there across the sea, and on the tenth day he was washed ashore on the island of Ogygia.

34

Love-In-Idleness

WILLIAM SHAKESPEARE

SINCE once I sat upon a promontory,
And heard a mermaid on a dolphin's back
Uttering such dulcet and harmonious breath
That the rude sea grew civil at her song.
And certain stars shot madly from their spheres,
To hear the sea-maid's music.

And the imperial votaress passed on,
In maiden meditation, fancy-free.
Yet mark'd I where the bolt of Cupid fell:
It fell upon a little western flower,
Before milk-white, now purple with love's wound,
And maidens call it love-in-idleness.

Of the Sprite, Undine

SARAH CHOKLA GROSS

UNDINE, also known as Ondine, water sprite whose name comes from the waves that are her home, those undulations called *unda* in Latin and *onde* in French, captured the fancy of a nineteenth century German novelist. Heinrich Karl de la Motte-Fouqué, drawing upon the undines of folklore for his chief character, wrote a romantic chronicle, *Undine*.

This story, enormously popular in its day, was a treat to Victorian readers in its English translation. When Charlotte Yonge was growing up—her book *The Little Duke* and other stories were to captivate children—*Undine* was a reward: when she read a sizeable chunk of serious history, she was allowed a chapter of *Undine* to balance it.

As Motte-Fouqué tells the story, Undine, a changeling, met a nobleman, Sir Huldbrand von Ringstetten, in the hut of a fisherman where she had come to take the place of the fisherman's daughter, Bertalda, thought to be drowned. Huldbrand married her, but by fairy law, Undine could keep the human form she had assumed only as long as her husband was true to her. If he cared for some other woman, Undine was doomed. As it happened, Bertalda had not drowned, and Huldbrand—attracted where he was not courted—determined to have her. Undine endured what she could not change until a day when, in a boat on the Danube, her husband sharply rebuked her. He lost her, for she left him, melting into that element from which she had come—the water, the waves.

Huldbrand, no example of depth or constancy, made ready to take Bertalda for his new wife. On his wedding eve, Undine rose from the water of a well, and with a parting kiss took the life of Huldbrand. As a limpid spring, the story has it, she circles his grave forever.

36

The Nix of
the Millpond

THE BROTHERS GRIMM

IN TIMES long gone by, there was a miller who lived with his wife in the greatest contentment and happiness. They had money and lands enough, and their prosperity increased year by year. But, as the proverb says, misfortune comes like a thief in the night—that is to say, when it is least expected. And so it was with the miller, for, as his riches had gradually increased, so did his wealth decrease, till, at last, he became so poor, that he could scarcely call his mill his own.

He was in great distress over his losses, and, although he

worked hard all day, he could get no rest at night, but tossed about on his bed unable to sleep.

One morning, he rose before daybreak, and went out, thinking that perhaps the fresh morning air would make his heart feel lighter. As he walked along the side of the milldam, the first rays of the sun were breaking forth, and he heard a rippling sound in the water behind him. He turned round, and saw a beautiful maiden rising slowly out of the stream. She held her long hair (which hung over her shoulders) back from her face with her soft, delicate hands, but allowed it to fall over her bosom, and cover her body like a veil. The miller at once recognized her as the nix, or water sprite, of the mill-pond, and in his fright at this unexpected apparition, he knew not whether to stay or to seek refuge in flight.

But the lovely phantom soon solved his doubts. She called him by name in a soft, gentle voice, and asked him why he was so sad. The miller was at first dumb, as though stupefied; but when he heard her speak so kindly to him, he took courage, and told her how he had once lived for many years in wealth and happiness, but that now he was so poor and so depressed in spirits that he knew not what to do.

"Let your mind be at rest," said the sprite, "I will make you richer and happier than you have ever been before; only you must promise to give me the first thing that is born in your house."

"That can be nothing else but a puppy or a kitten," thought the miller; so he at once promised her what she desired. Thereupon the water-sprite immediately dived under the water, and the miller hastened homeward, animated and consoled.

He had almost reached the mill when he met his wife's maid-servant. She was hastening towards him with the joyful news of the birth of a son and heir. On hearing this, the miller started back as if struck by lightning, for he at once comprehended that the cunning and malicious nix had acted deceitfully towards him.

He went at once to his wife's room, and, full of trouble, with his head bowed down, he told her all that had occurred, and what a dreadful promise he had given to the nix.

"Of what use are all the riches and good luck in the world to us," he said, "if we are to lose our dear boy? What must we do?" And none of his relations, who came to congratulate him on the birth of a son and heir, could give him any advice.

In the meantime prosperity again returned to the miller's house. Everything he undertook succeeded; it was as if his chests and coffers filled themselves of their own accord, and as if money multiplied in his desk during the night so that in a short time, the miller was richer than he had ever been before.

But his affluence brought him no happiness, for his promise to the water sprite weighed on his mind, and tormented his soul. Whenever he passed the milldam he dreaded lest she should ascend out of the water, and remind him of his debt. He gave orders that his son was never to be allowed to go near the water, and often told him to beware of doing so, for, if he should fall in, a hand would rise up, and drag him under. Still, as year after year rolled by, and the water sprite made no second appearance, the miller began to lose his suspicions, and felt more at ease.

The boy grew up a fine youth. He was apprenticed to a huntsman and as he was a clever lad, and soon became expert with his gun, the nobleman of the village took him into his service. In this village lived a beautiful and true-hearted maiden, whom the young man asked in marriage; and when his master heard of this, he gave them a pretty little cottage, where they lived, after their marriage, in peace and contentment, sincerely loving each other with all the fondness of their true hearts.

One day the young man was pursuing a stag, when the animal escaped from the forest into the open fields; here he overtook it, and with a single shot, succeeded in bringing it to the ground. He was so earnestly engaged in his sport, that he failed to notice he had reached the brink of the dangerous mill pond. When he had killed the stag, flayed it, and cut it up, he went to the water to wash his blood-stained hands. Scarcely, however, had he dipped them in when the nix arose, and with her dripping arms smilingly embraced him, and drew him so quickly below the surface, that neither a ripple, nor a bubble, showed where he had gone.

When evening came, and the hunter did not return home, his wife became anxious, feeling alarmed at his absence. At last she went out to seek him, and as he had often told her how he had to be on his guard against the snares of the water sprite, and that he dared not venture too near the mill stream, she suspected what had happened.

She hastened at once to the water, and, on arriving at the bank of the stream, she saw her husband's hunting pouch lying on the grass and could no longer have any doubt of the misfortune which had come upon him. Wringing her hands in grief and terror, and with loud lamentations, she called her beloved by name, again and again, but in vain. She hurried across to the other side of the pond; she alternately entreated and scolded the nix, and reviled her with harsh words, but no answer followed. The surface of the water remained as smooth as a mirror, in which the crescent moon was clearly reflected.

The poor wife was reluctant to leave the millstream. With quick and hasty steps she walked up and down the bank without ceasing, now in silence, now softly sobbing, and ever and anon uttering loud cries of despair. At last her strength failed her, and, worn out with grief and fatigue, she sank wearily to the ground, fell into a deep sleep and dreamed a wonderful dream.

She thought she was anxiously climbing upwards, between great masses of rock. Thorns and briers pierced her feet, the rain beat in her face, and the wind tossed her long hair about in wild confusion. When she had reached the summit, quite a different scene presented itself. The sky was blue and serene, and the air balmy, the ground sloped gently downwards, and, on a green meadow, spangled with bright flowers, stood an elegant cottage. She went up to it, and opened the door; there sat, as she thought, an old woman, with white hair, who beckoned to her kindly to come in. But just at that moment the poor wife awoke from her dream.

Day was already dawning, and she knew she had slept a considerable time. She felt refreshed, and called to mind that a mountain, such as she had dreamed about, was not far distant. She at once resolved to act in accordance with her dream, and turned her steps towards it. After laboriously climbing up, she reached the top, and found the verdant meadow, and the cottage, exactly as it had appeared in her dream.

The old woman received her with the utmost kindness, and, pointing to a chair, requested her to be seated. "You must have met with some great misfortune," she said, "since you have sought out my lonely cottage. What is it?"

The wife related to her with tears in her eyes, all that had befallen her. "Be comforted, my dear," said the old woman. "I will help you. Here is a golden comb; wait, till the full moon is risen, then go to the millpond, sit down on the bank, and comb out your long black hair with it. When you have done, lay the comb down on the bank, and you will see what will happen."

The woman returned home, but the time passed slowly till the moon became full. At last the longed-for night arrived; the moon's shining disc appeared in the heavens, and she went down to the mill-pond, seated herself on the bank, and began combing her long black hair with the golden comb. When she had finished, she laid the comb down near the edge of the stream, and awaited the issue.

It was not long before there was a movement in the depths of the water, a wave rose, rolled to the bank, and, as it receded, carried away the golden comb. In not more time than it was necessary for the comb to have sunk to the bottom, the surface of the water was divided and the head of the huntsman arose above it. He looked sorrowfully at his wife; but, before he could speak, a second wave came rushing up and covered his head. All then disappeared; the millpond lay as tranquil and calm as before, and nothing was to be seen but the reflection of the pale moon on its placid surface.

Full of sorrow the poor woman returned home; all her hopes were fled; but during the night her dreams again showed her the cottage beyond the mountains. So, next morning, she once more set out to visit the wise woman, and lay her complaints and sorrows, before her.

As before, the old woman comforted her, and, giving her a golden flute, directed her to wait for the next full moon. She was then to take the flute, betake herself to the shore of the pond, and play a beautiful air upon it; that finished, she was to lay the flute on the sand near the edge of the water, and wait the result as before.

The huntsman's wife followed these directions implicitly. No sooner had she finished her music, and placed the flute on the shore, than the water began to be agitated as before, and a huge wave rushed up and carried the flute away with it. Immediately afterwards the water divided, and not only the head, but nearly half the body of her husband, appeared above the surface. He stretched out his arms lovingly towards her, but, at the same instant, a second wave rose, and, with a rushing sound, covered the poor man, and drew him under again.

"Alas!" cried the unhappy woman, "what does it profit me to only have a passing glance at my dear husband, and then to lose him again!" Intense grief took possession of her heart, anew, and overcame her; but her dreams led her a third time to the cottage, and the old woman, and her hopes revived. Accordingly she paid her another visit in the morning.

This time the wise woman gave her a golden spinning wheel, and, consoling her, said: "All that is necessary has not yet been done. You must tarry till the time of the next full moon; then, taking the golden spinning wheel with you, seat yourself on the shore, and spin industriously till the spools are full. When this is done, place the wheel near the water's edge and wait the result."

The wife followed out all these directions with the utmost exactness; but when she had obediently carried out her instructions, and placed the spinning wheel on the shore, the water bubbled up more violently than ever. An immense wave arose, and, dashing up to the wheel, swept it away in a moment. No sooner had it disappeared than the head, and then the whole body, of the huntsman rose above the water. Like a flash of lightning, he sprang ashore, caught his wife by the hand, and fled away with her.

They had only gone a few steps, when the whole water in the pond rose, and, with a terrible rushing noise, and irresistible force, spread itself over the open country. The two fugitives saw nothing but death before them. The wife, in her terror, implored the help of the old woman, and just as they were giving themselves up for lost, they were in an instant transformed—the woman into a frog, the husband into a toad. The flood, which had overtaken them, could not destroy them; but though they escaped death, the waters bore them asunder, and carried them far away from each other in opposite directions.

When the waters subsided again, and the toad and frog touched dry ground, they each resumed their proper human form, but neither of them knew what had become of the other. They found themselves in a strange country among foreigners, who did not know their native land. High mountains and deep valleys lay between them, and, in order to earn a livelihood, they were each obliged to tend sheep. For many long years they drove their flocks and herds through fields and forests, weighed down with sorrow, grieving at being separated, and longing to see each other.

And so the years passed on. But when once again the sweet breath of spring covered the earth with lovely flowers, it chanced that they both drove out their herds, on the same day, towards the same point. The former huntsman, perceiving a flock of sheep grazing on the green hillside, led his own flock towards the same spot. Thus the two flocks came together in a valley, but without their keepers recognizing each other; still the two lonely ones each rejoiced to find they had no longer to wander in solitude and loneliness. From that day they drove their flocks together to the same pasture, and though they did not talk much, they felt the utmost comfort and consolation in each other's society.

One evening, when the full moon was shining in the sky, and the flocks were already resting, the shepherd drew a flute out of his pocket, and began playing a sweet but mournful air upon it.

When he had finished, he saw that the shepherdess, who was seated at his side, was weeping bitterly. The music revived in her memories of past times, and her companion anxiously asked the reason for her grief.

"Alas!" she replied, "thus shone the full moon in the sky the last

43

time I played that air on my flute, and the head of my beloved one rose above the water."

The shepherd looked at her with a steadfast and earnest gaze as she spoke; it seemed as if a veil fell from before his eyes, and he perceived she was his beloved and long-lost wife. The moon shone brightly on his face, and she recognized him at the same moment. They instantly embraced and kissed each other with fervent joy, and I am sure no one needs to ask if they were happy in one another's society, now they had been so wonderfully restored to each other.

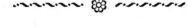

The Island Mist

GEORGE WALDRON

A MERMAID becoming enamored of a young man of extraordinary beauty, took an opportunity of meeting him one day as he walked on the shore of the Isle of Man, and told him of her love, but was received with a coldness occasioned by his horror and surprise at her appearance. This, however, was so misconstrued by the sea lady that, in revenge for his treatment of her, she punished the whole Island by covering it with a mist; so that all who attempted to carry on any commerce with it, either never arrived at it, but wandered up and down the sea, or were all of a sudden wrecked upon its cliffs.

Little John Bottlejohn

LAURA E. RICHARDS

Little John Bottlejohn lived on the hill,
    And a blithe little man was he.
And he won the heart of a pretty mermaid
    Who lived in the deep blue sea.
And every evening she used to sit
    And sing on the rocks by the sea,
"Oh, little John Bottlejohn, pretty John Bottlejohn,
    Won't you come out to me?"

Little John Bottlejohn heard her song,
    And he opened his little door.
And he hopped and he skipped, and he skipped and he hopped,
    Until he came down to the shore.
And there on the rocks sat the little mermaid,
    And still she was singing so free,
"Oh! little John Bottlejohn, pretty John Bottlejohn,
    Won't you come out to me?"

Little John Bottlejohn made a bow,
    And the mermaid, she made one too;
And she said, "Oh! I never saw any one half
    So perfectly sweet as you!
In my lovely home 'neath the ocean foam,
    How happy we both might be!
Oh! little John Bottlejohn, pretty John Bottlejohn,
    Won't you come down with me?"

Little John Bottlejohn said, "Oh yes!
    I'll willingly go with you.
And I never shall quail at the sight of your tail,
    For perhaps I may grow one too."
So he took her hand, and he left the land,
    And plunged in the foaming main.
And little John Bottlejohn, pretty John Bottlejohn,
    Never was seen again.

Daniel Webster
and
the Sea Serpent

STEPHEN VINCENT BENÉT

IT HAPPENED, one summer's day, that Dan'l Webster and some of his friends were out fishing. That was in the high days of his power and his fame, when the question wasn't if he was going to be President but when he was going to be President, and everybody at Kingston depot stood up when Dan'l Webster arrived to take the cars. But in spite of being Secretary of State and the biggest man in New England, he was just the same Dan'l Webster. He bought his Jamaica personal and in the jug at Colonel Sever's store in Kingston, right under a sign

47

saying ENGLISH AND WEST INDIA GOODS, and he never was too busy to do a hand's turn for a friend. And, as for his big farm at Marsh-field, that was just the apple of his eye. He buried his favorite horses with their shoes on, standing up, in a private graveyard, and wrote Latin epitaphs for them, and he often was heard to say that his big Hungarian bull, Saint Stephen, had more sense in his rear off hoof than most politicians. But, if there was one thing he loved better than Marshfield itself, it was the sea and the waters around it, for he was a fisherman born.

This time, he was saltwater fishing in the Comet, well out of sight of land. It was a good day for fishing, not too hazy, but not too clear, and Dan'l Webster enjoyed it, as he enjoyed everything in life, ex-cept maybe listening to the speeches of Henry Clay. He'd stolen a half-dozen days to come up to Marshfield, and well he needed the rest, for we'd nearly gone to war with England the year before, and now he was trying to fix up a real copper-riveted treaty that would iron out all the old differences that still kept the two countries un-friendly And that was a job, even for Dan'l Webster. But as soon as he stepped aboard the Comet, he was carefree and heartwhole. He had his real friends around him and he wouldn't allow a word of politics talked on the boat—though that rule got broken this time, and for a good reason, as you'll see. And when he struck his first cod, and felt the fish take the hook, a kind of big slow smile went over his features, and he said, "Gentlemen, this is solid comfort." That was the kind of man he was.

I don't know how many there were of them aboard—half a dozen or so—just enough for good company. We'll say there were George Blake and Rufus Choate and young Peter Harvey and a boy named Jim Billings. And, of course, there was Seth Peterson, Dan'l's boat captain, in his red flannel shirt, New England as cod and beach plums, and Dan'l Webster's fast friend. Dan'l happened to be Secre-tary of State, and Seth Peterson happened to be a boat captain, but that didn't make any difference between them. And, once the Comet left dock, Seth Peterson ran the show, as it's right that a captain should.

Well, they'd fished all morning and knocked off for a bite of lunch, and some had had segars and snoozes afterward, and some hadn't, but in any case, it was around midafternoon, and everybody was kind of comfortable and contented. They still fished, and they fished well, but they knew in an hour or so they'd be heading back for home with a fine catch on board. So maybe there was more conversation than Seth Peterson would have approved of earlier, and maybe some jokes were passed and some stories told. I don't know, but you know how it is when men get together at the end of a good day. All the same, they were still paying attention to their business— and I guess it was George Blake that noticed it first.

"Dan'l," he said, breathing hard, "I've got something on my line that pulls like a Morgan horse."

"Well, yank him in!" sang out Dan'l, and then his face changed as his own line began to stiffen and twang. "George," he said, "I beat you! I got something on my line that pulls like a pair of steers!"

"Give 'em more line, Mr. Webster!" yells Seth Peterson, and Dan'l did. But at that, the line ran out so fast it smoked when it hit the water, and any hands but Dan'l Webster's would have been cut to the bone. Nor you couldn't see where it went to, except Something deep in the waters must be pulling it out as a cat pulls yarn from a ball. The veins in Dan'l Webster's arm stood out like cords. He played the fish and played the fish; he fought it with every trick he knew. And still the little waves danced and the other men gaped at the fight—and still he couldn't bring the Something to time.

"By the big elm at Marshfield!" he said at last, with his dark face glowing and a fisherman's pride in his eyes. "Have I hooked on to a frigate with all sails set? I've payed out a mile of my own particular line, and she still pulls like ten wild horses. Gentlemen, what's this?"

And even as he said it, the tough line broke in two with a crack like a musket shot, and out of the deep of ocean, a mile away, the creature rose, majestic. Neighbors, that was a sight! Shaking the hook from its jaw, it rose, the sea serpent of the Scriptures, exact and to specifications as laid down in the Good Book, with its hairy face and its furlong on furlong of body, wallowing and thrashing in the troubled sea. As it rose, it gave a long low melancholy hoot, like a kind of forsaken steamboat; and when it gave out that hoot, young Jim Billings, the boy, fainted dead away on the deck. But nobody even noticed him—they were all staring at the sea serpent with bulging eyes.

Even Dan'l Webster was shaken. He passed his hand for a moment across his brow and gave a sort of inquiring look at the jug of Jamaica by the hatch.

"Gentlemen," he said in a low voice, "the evidence—the ocular evidence would seem to be conclusive. And yet, speaking as a lawyer—"

"Thar she blows! I never thought to see her again!" yells Seth Peterson, half driven out of his mind by the sight, as the sea serpent roiled the waters. "Thar she blows, by the Book of Genesis! Oh, why ain't I got a harpoon?"

"Quiet, Seth," said Dan'l Webster. "Let us rather give thanks for being permitted to witness this glorious and unbelievable sight." And then you could see the real majesty of the man, for no sooner were the words out of his mouth than the sea serpent started swimming straight toward the Comet. She came like a railway train and her wake boiled out behind her for an acre. And yet, there was something kind of skittish about her, too—you might say that she came kind of shaking her skirts and bridling. I don't know what there was about her that made you sure she was a female, but they were all sure.

She came, direct as a bullet, till you could count the white teeth shining in her jaws. I don't know what the rest of them did—though doubtless some prayers were put up in a hasty way—but Dan'l Webster stood there and faced her, with his brow dark and his eyes like a sleepy lion's, giving her glance for glance. Yes, there was a minute, there, when she lifted her head high out of water and they looked at each other eye to eye. They say hers were reddish but handsome. And then, just as it seemed she'd crash plumb through the Comet, she made a wide wheel and turned. Three times she circled the boat, hooting lonesomely, while the Comet danced up and down like a cork on the waves. But Dan'l Webster kept his footing, one hand gripping the mast, and whenever he got a chance, he fixed her with his eye. Till finally, on the third circuit, she gave one last long hoot—like twenty foghorns at once, it was, and nearly deafened them all—and plunged back whence she'd come, to the bottomless depths of the sea.

But even after the waters were calm again, they didn't say anything for quite a while. Till, finally, Seth Peterson spoke.

"Well, Mr. Webster," he said, "that one got away"—and he grinned a dry grin.

"Leviathan of the Scriptures! Give me paper and pen," said Dan'l Webster. "We must write this down and attest it." And then they all began to talk.

Well, he wrote an account of just what they'd seen, very plain and honest. And everybody there signed his name to it. Then he read it over to them again aloud. And then there was another silence, while they looked at one another.

Finally, Seth Peterson shook his head, slow and thoughtful.

"It won't do, Dan'l," he said, in a deep voice.

"Won't do?" said Dan'l Webster, with his eyes blazing. "What do you mean, Seth?"

"I mean it just won't do, Dan'l," said Seth Peterson, perfectly respectful, but perfectly firm. "I put it up to you, gentlemen," he said, turning to the others. "I can go home and say I've seen the sea serpent. And everybody'll say, 'Oh, that's just that old liar, Seth Peterson.' But if it's Dan'l Webster says so—can't you see the difference?"

He paused for a minute, but nobody said a word.

"Well, I can," he said. He drawled out the words very slow. "Dan'l Webster—Secretary of State—sees and talks to a sea serpent— off Plymouth Bay. Why, it would plumb ruin him! And I don't mind being ruint, but it's different with Dan'l Webster. Would you vote for a man for President who claimed he'd saw the sea serpent? Well, would you? Would anybody?"

There was another little silence, and then George Blake spoke.

51

"He's right, Dan'l," he said, while the others nodded. "Give me that paper." He took it from Dan'l Webster's hand and threw it in the sea.

"And now," he said in a firm voice, "I saw cod. Nothing but cod. Except maybe a couple of halibut. Did any gentleman here see anything else?"

Well, at that, it turned out, of course, that nobody aboard had seen anything but cod all day. And with that, they put back for shore. All the same, they all looked over their shoulders a good deal till they got back to harbor.

And yet Dan'l Webster wasn't too contented that evening, in spite of his fine catch. For, after all, he had seen the sea serpent, and not only seen her but played her on the line for twenty-seven minutes by his gold repeater, and, being a fisherman, he'd like to have said so. And yet, if he did—Seth was right—folks would think him crazy or worse. It took his mind off Lord Ashburton and the treaty with England—till, finally, he pushed aside the papers on his desk.

"Oh, a plague on the beast!" he said, kind of crossly. "I'll leave it alone and hope it leaves me alone." So he took his candle and went up to bed. But just as he was dropping off to sleep, he thought he heard a long low hoot from the mouth of Green Harbor River, two miles away.

The next night the hooting continued, and the third day there was a piece in the Kingston paper about the new Government foghorn at Rocky Ledge. Well, the thing began to get on Dan'l Webster's nerves, and when his temper was roused he wasn't a patient man. Moreover, the noises seemed to disturb the stock—at least his overseer said so—and the third night his favorite gray kicked half the door out of her stall. "That sea serpent's getting to be an infernal nuisance," thought Dan'l Webster. "I've got to protect my property." So, the fourth night he put on his old duck-shooting clothes and took his favorite shotgun, Learned Selden, and went down to a blind at the mouth of Green Harbor River, to see what he could see. He didn't tell anybody else about his intentions, because he still felt kind of sensitive about the whole affair.

52

Well, there was a fine moon that night, and sure enough, about eleven o'clock, the sea serpent showed up, steaming in from ocean, all one continuous wave length, like a giant garden hose. She was quite a handsome sight, all speckled with the moonlight, but Dan'l Webster couldn't rightly appreciate it. And just as she came to the blind, she lifted her head and looked sorrowfully in the direction of Marshfield and let out a long low soulful hoot like a homesick train.

Dan'l Webster hated to do it. But he couldn't have a sea serpent living in Green Harbor River and scaring the stock—not to speak of the universal consternation and panic there'd be in the countryside when such a thing was known. So he lifted Learned Selden and gave her both barrels for a starter, just a trifle over her head. And as soon as the gun exploded, the sea serpent let out a screech you could hear a mile and headed back for open sea. If she'd traveled fast before, she traveled like lightning now, and it wasn't any time before she was just a black streak on the waters.

Dan'l Webster stepped out of the blind and wiped his brow. He felt sorry, but he felt relieved. He didn't think she'd be back, after that sort of scare, and he wanted to leave everything shipshape before he went down to Washington, next morning. But next day, when he told Seth Peterson what he'd done, he didn't feel so chipper. For, "You shouldn't have done that, Mr. Webster," said Seth Peterson, shaking his head, and that was all he would say except a kind of mutter that sounded like "Samanthy was always particular set in her likes." But Dan'l didn't pay any attention to that, though he remembered it later, and he was quite short with Seth for the first time in their long relationship. So Seth shut up like a quahog, and Dan'l took the cars for Washington.

When he got there he was busy enough, for the British treaty was on the boil, and within twenty-four hours he'd forgot all about the sea serpent. Or thought he had. But three days later, as he was walking home to his house on Lafayette Square, with a senator friend of his, in the cool of the evening, they heard a curious noise. It seemed to come from the direction of the Potomac River.

53

"Must have got a new whistle for the Baltimore night boat," said the senator. "Noisy too."

"Oh, that's just the bullfrogs on the banks," said Dan'l Webster steadily. But he knew what it was, just the same, and his heart sank within him. But nobody ever called Dan'l Webster a coward. So, as soon as he'd got rid of the senator, he went down to the banks of the Potomac. Well, it was the sea serpent, all right.

She looked a little tired, as well she might, having swum from Plymouth Bay. But as soon as she saw Dan'l Webster, she stretched out her neck and gave a long low loving hoot. Then Dan'l knew what the trouble was and, for once in his life, he didn't know what to do. But he'd brought along a couple of roe herring, in a paper, just in case; so he fed them to her and she hooted, affectionate and grateful. Then he walked back to his house with his head bowed. And that very night he sent a special express letter to Seth Peterson at Marshfield, for, it seemed to him, Seth must know more about the business than he let on.

Well, Seth got to Washington as fast as the cars would bring him, and the very evening he arrived Dan'l sent him over to interview the serpent. But when Seth came back, Dan'l could see by his face that he hadn't made much progress.

"Could you talk to her, Seth?" he said, and his voice was eager. "Can she understand United States?"

"Oh, she can understand it all right," said Seth. "She's even picking up a few words. They was always a smart family, those Rock Ledge serpents, and she's the old maid of the lot, and the best educated. The only trouble with 'em is, they're so terrible sot in their ways."

"You might have warned me, Seth," said Dan'l Webster, kind of reproachful, and Seth looked uncomfortable.

"Well, to tell you the truth," he said, "I thought all of 'em was dead. Nor I never thought she'd act up like this—her father was as respectable a serpent as you'd see in a long summer's day. Her father—"

"Bother her father!" said Dan'l Webster and set his jaw. "Tell me

54

what she says."

"Well, Mr. Webster," said Seth, and stared at his boots, "she says you're quite a handsome man. She says she never did see anybody quite like you," he went on. "I hate to tell you this, Mr. Webster, and I feel kind of responsible, but I think you ought to know. And I told you that you oughtn't to have shot at her—she's pretty proud of that. She says she knows just how you meant it. Well, I'm no great hand at being embarrassed, Mr. Webster, but, I tell you, she embarrassed me. You see, she's been an old maid for about a hundred and fifty years, I guess, and that's the worst of it. And being the last of her folks in those particular waters, there's just no way to restrain her—her father and mother was as sensible, hardworking serpents as ever gave a feller a tow through a fog, but you know how it is with those old families. Well, she says wherever you go, she'll follow you, and she claims she wants to hear you speak before the Supreme Court—"

"Did you tell her I'm a married man?" said Dan'l. "Did you tell her that?"

"Yes, I told her," said Seth, and you could see the perspiration on his forehead. "But she says that doesn't signify—her being a serpent and different—and she's fixing to move right in. She says Washington's got a lovely climate and she's heard all about the balls and the diplomatic receptions. I don't know how she's heard about them, but she has." He swallowed. "I got her to promise she'd kind of lie low for two weeks and not come up the Potomac by daylight—she was fixing to do that because she wants to meet the President. Well, I got her to promise that much. But she says, even so, if you don't come to see her once an evening, she'll hoot till you do, and she told me to tell you that you haven't heard hooting yet. And as soon as the fish market's open, I better run down and buy a barrel of flaked cod, Mr. Webster—she's partial to flaked cod and she usually takes it in the barrel. Well, I don't want to worry you, Mr. Webster, but I'm afraid that we're in a fix."

"A fix!" said Dan'l Webster. "It's the biggest fix I ever was in in my life!"

"Well, it's kind of complimentary, in a way, I guess," said Seth Peterson, "but—"

"Does she say anything else?" said Dan'l Webster, drawing a long breath.

"Yes, Mr. Webster," said Seth Peterson, his eyes on his boots. "She says you're a little shy. But she says she likes that in a man."

Dan'l Webster went to bed that night, but he didn't sleep. He worked and worked those great brains of his till he nearly wore out the wheels, but he still couldn't think of a way to get rid of the sea serpent. And just about the time dawn broke, he heard one long low hoot, faithful and reminiscent, from the direction of the Potomac.

Well, the next two weeks were certainly bad ones for him. For, as the days wore on, the sea serpent got more and more restive. She wanted him to call her Samanthy, which he wouldn't, and she kept asking him when he was going to introduce her into society, till he had to feed her Italian sardines in olive oil to keep her quiet. And that ran up a bill at the fish market that he hated to think of—besides, her continually threatening to come up the Potomac by day. Moreover, and to put the cap on things, the great Webster-Ashburton treaty that was to make his name as Secretary of State had struck a snag and England didn't seem at all partial to admitting the American claims. Oh, it was a weary fortnight and a troublesome one!

The last afternoon of the fortnight, he sat in his office and he didn't know where to turn. For Lord Ashburton was coming to see him for a secret conference that night at nine, and he had to see the sea serpent at ten, and how to satisfy either of them he didn't know. His eyes stared wearily at the papers on his desk. He rang the bell for his secretary.

"The corvette Benjamin Franklin reports—" he said. "This should have gone to the Navy Department, Mr. Jones." Then he glanced at the naval report again and his eyes began to glow like furnaces. "By the bones of Leviathan! I've got it!" he said, with a shout. "Where's my hat, Mr. Jones. I must see the President at once!"

There was a different feeling about the house on Lafayette Square that evening, for Dan'l Webster was himself again. He cracked a joke with Seth Peterson and took a glass of Madeira and turned it to the light. And when Lord Ashburton was announced—a nice, white-haired old gentleman, though a little stiff in his joints—he received him with all the courtesy of a king.

"I am glad to see you so much restored, Mr. Webster," said Lord Ashburton, when the greetings had been exchanged. "And yet I fear I bring you bad news. Concerning clauses six and seven of the proposed treaty between Her Majesty's Government and the United States of America, it is my duty to state—"

"My lord, let us drop the clauses for a moment and take the wider view," said Dan'l Webster, smiling. "This is a matter concerning the future welfare and peace of two great nations. Your government claims the right to search our ships; that right we deny. And our attitude seems to you preposterous. Is that not so?"

"I would hesitate to use the word 'preposterous,'" said Lord Ashburton cautiously. "Yet—"

"And yet," said Dan'l Webster, leaning forward, "there are things which may seem preposterous, and yet are not. Let me put a case. Let us say that Great Britain has the strongest navy afloat."

"Britannia rules the waves," said Lord Ashburton, with a noble smile.

"There were a couple she didn't rule in 1812," said Dan'l Webster, "but let that pass. Let me ask you, Lord Ashburton, and let me ask you solemnly, what could even the power and might of Britain's navy avail against Leviathan?"

"Leviathan?" said Lord Ashburton, rather coldly. "Naturally, I understand the Biblical allusion. Yet—"

"The sea serpent," said Dan'l Webster, kind of impatient. "What could all Britain's navy do against the sea serpent out of the Scriptures?"

Lord Ashburton stared at him as if he had gone mad. "God bless my soul, Mr. Secretary!" he said. "But I fail to see the point of your question. The sea serpent doesn't exist!"

"Doesn't he—I mean she?" said Dan'l Webster, calmly. "And suppose I should prove to you that it does exist?"

"Well, 'pon my word! God bless my soul!" said Lord Ashburton, kind of taken aback. "Naturally—in that case—however—but even so—"

Dan'l Webster touched a bell on his desk. "Lord Ashburton," he said, kind of solemn, "I am putting my life, and what is dearer to me, my honor and reputation, in your hands. Nevertheless, I feel it necessary, for a better understanding between our two countries."

Seth Peterson came into the room and Dan'l nodded at him.

"Seth," he said, "Lord Ashburton is coming with us to see Samanthy."

"It's all right if you say so, Mr. Webster," said Seth Peterson, "but he'll have to help carry the sardines."

"Well, 'pon my word! Bless my soul! A very strange proceeding!" said Lord Ashburton, but he followed along.

Well, they got to the banks of the Potomac, the three of them, and when they were there, Seth whistled. Samanthy was lying mostly under water, behind a little brushy island, but when she heard the whistle, she began to heave up and uncoil, all shining in the moonlight. It was what you might call a kind of impressive sight. Dan'l Webster looked at Lord Ashburton, but Lord Ashburton's words seemed sort of stuck in his throat.

Finally he got them out. "Bless my soul!" he said. "You Americans are very extraordinary! Is it alive?"

But then all he could do was goggle, for Samanthy had lifted her head, and giving a low friendly hoot, she commenced to swim around the island.

"Now, is that a sea serpent or isn't it?" said Dan'l Webster, with a kind of quiet pride.

"Indubitably," said Lord Ashburton, staring through his eyeglass. "Indubitably," and he kind of cleared his throat. "It is, indeed and in fact, a serpent of the sea. And I am asleep and in bed, in my room at the British Embassy." He pinched himself. "Ouch!" he said. "No, I am not."

"Would you call it sizable, for a sea serpent?" persisted Dan'l Webster.

Lord Ashburton stared again through his eyeglass. "Quite," he said. "Oh, yes, quite, quite!"

"And powerful?" asked Dan'l.

"I should judge so," said Lord Ashburton, faintly, as the sea serpent swam around and around the island and the waves of its wake broke crashing on the bank. "Yes, indeed, a very powerful engine of destruction. May I ask what it feeds upon?"

"Italian sardines, for preference," said Dan'l. "But that's beside the point." He drew a long breath. "Well, my lord," he said, "we're intending to commission that sea serpent as a regular and acknowledged war vessel in the United States Navy. And then, where's your wooden walls?"

Lord Ashburton, he was a diplomat, and his face didn't change expression as he stared first at the sea serpent and then at the face of Dan'l Webster. But after a while, he nodded. "You need not labor the point, Mr. Secretary," he said. "My government, I am sure, will be glad to reconsider its position on the last two clauses and on the right of search."

"Then I'm sure we can reach an agreement," said Dan'l Webster, and wiped the sweat from his brow. "And now, let's feed Samanthy."

He whistled to her himself, a long musical whistle, and she came bounding and looping in toward shore. It took all three of them to heave her the barrel of sardines, and she swallowed it down in one gulp. After that, she gave a hoot of thanks and gratitude, and Lord Ashburton sat down on the bank for a minute and took snuff. He said that he needed something to clear his mind.

"Naturally," he said, after a while, "Her Majesty's Government must have adequate assurances as to the good conduct of this—this lady." He'd meant to say "creature" at first, but Samanthy rolled her eye at him just then, and he changed the word.

"You shall have them," said Dan'l Webster, and whistled Samanthy even closer. She came in kind of skittish, flirting her coils, and Lord Ashburton closed his eyes for a minute. But when Dan'l Webster spoke, it was in the voice that hushed the Senate whenever he rose.

59

"Samanthy," he said, "I speak to you now as Secretary of State of the United States of America." It was the great voice that had rung in the Supreme Court and replied to Hayne, and even a sea serpent had to listen respectful. For the voice was mellow and deep, and he pictured Samanthy's early years as a carefree young serpent, playing with her fellows, and then her hard life of toil and struggle when she was left lone and lorn, till even Seth Peterson and Lord Ashburton realized the sorrow and tragedy of her lonely lot. And then, in the gentlest and kindest way you could ask, he showed her where her duty lay.

"For, if you keep on hooting in the Potomac, Samanthy," he said, "you'll become a public menace to navigation and get sat upon by the Senate Committee for Rivers and Harbors. They'll drag you up on land, Samanthy, and put you in the Smithsonian Institution; they'll stick you in a stagnant little pool and children will come to throw you peanuts on Sundays, and their nurses will poke you with umbrellas if you don't act lively enough. The U. S. Navy will shoot at you for target practice, Samanthy, and the scientists will examine you, and the ladies of the Pure Conduct League will knit you a bathing suit, and you'll be bothered every minute by congressmen and professors and visitors and foreign celebrities till you won't be able to call your scales your own. Oh, yes, it'll be fame, Samanthy, but it won't be good enough. Believe me, I know something about fame and it's begging letters from strangers and calls from people you don't know and don't want to know, and the burden and wear and tear of being a public character till it's enough to break your heart. It isn't good enough, Samanthy; it won't give you back your free waters and your sporting in the deep. Yes, Samanthy, it'd be a remarkable thing to have you here in Washington, but it isn't the life you were meant for and I can't take advantage of your trust. And now," he said to Seth Peterson, "just what does she say?"

Seth Peterson listened, attentive, to the hootings.

"She says the Washington climate isn't what she thought it was," he said. "And the Potomac River's too warm; it's bad for her sciatica. And she's plumb tired of sardines."

"Does she say anything about me?" asked Dan'l Webster, anxiously.

"Well," said Seth Peterson, listening, "she says—if you'll excuse me, Mr. Webster—that you may be a great man, but you wouldn't make much of a sea serpent. She says you haven't got enough coils. She says—well, she says no hard feelings, but she guesses it was a mistake on both sides."

He listened again. "But she says one thing," he said. "She says she's got to have recognition and a husband, if she has to take this Lord Ashburton. She says he doesn't look like much, but he might get her introduced at Court."

A great light broke over Dan'l's face and his voice rang out like thunder. "She shall have them both," he said. "Come here, Samanthy. By virtue of the authority vested in me as Secretary of State, and by special order of the President of the United States and the Secretary of the Navy, as witness the attached commission in blank which I now fill in with your name, I hereby attach you to the United States Navy, to rank as a forty-four-gun frigate on special duty, rating a rear admiral's flag and a salute of the appropriate number of guns, wherever encountered in American waters. And, by virtue of the following special order, I hereby order you to the South Seas, there to cruise until further orders for the purpose of seeking a suitable and proper husband, with all the rights, privileges, duties and appurtenances pertaining to said search and said American citizenship, as aforesaid and Hail Columbia. Signed John Tyler, President. With which is subjoined a passport signed by Daniel Webster, Secretary of State, bidding all foreign nations let pass without hindrance the American citizen, Samanthy Doe, on her lawful journeys and errands." He dropped his voice for a moment and added reflectively, "The American corvette, Benjamin Franklin, reports sighting a handsome young male sea serpent on February third of the present year, just off the coast of the Sandwich Islands. Said serpent had forty-two coils by actual count, and when last sighted was swimming SSW at full speed."

But hardly had he spoken when Samanthy, for the last time,

61

lifted her head and gave out a last long hoot. She looked upon Dan'l Webster as she did so, and there was regret in her eye. But the regret was tinctured with eagerness and hope.

Then she beat the water to a froth, and, before they really saw her go, she was gone, leaving only her wake on the moonlit Potomac.

"Well," said Dan'l Webster, yawning a little, "there we are. And now, Lord Ashburton, if you'll come home with me, we can draw up that treaty."

"Gladly," said Lord Ashburton, brushing his coat with his handkerchief. "Is it really gone? 'Pon my soul! You know, for a moment, I imagined that I actually saw a sea serpent. You have a very vivid way of putting things, Mr. Webster. But I think I understand the American attitude now, from the—er—analogy you were pleased to draw between such a—er—fabulous animal and the young strength of your growing country."

"I was confident that you would appreciate it, once it was brought to your attention," said Dan'l Webster. But he winked one eye at Seth Peterson, and Seth Peterson winked back.

And I'll say this for Dan'l Webster, too—he kept his promises. All through the time he was Secretary of State, he saw to it that the forty-four-gun frigate, Samanthy Doe, was carried on a special account on the books of the Navy. In fact, there's some people say that she's still so carried, and that it was she who gave Ericsson the idea for building the Monitor in the Civil War—if she wasn't the Monitor herself. And when the White Fleet went around the world in Teddy Roosevelt's time—well, there was a lookout in the crow's nest of the flagship, one still calm night, as they passed by the palmy isles of the South Seas. And all of a sudden, the water boiled, tremendous and phosphorescent, and there was a pair of sea serpents and seven young ones, circling, calm and majestic, three times around the fleet. He rubbed his eyes and he stared, but there they were. Well, he was the only one that saw it, and they put him in the brig for it next morning. But he swore, till the day he died, they were flying the Stars and Stripes.

A Sea Dirge

WILLIAM SHAKESPEARE

Full fathom five thy father lies:
  Of his bones are coral made;
Those are pearls that were his eyes:
  Nothing of him that doth fade
But doth suffer a sea-change
Into something rich and strange.
Sea-nymphs hourly ring his knell:
Hark! now I hear them,—
        Ding, dong, bell.

The Plunderer

JOHN MASEFIELD

L YING on the bottom, partly on white sand, partly among coral and weed, was the wreck of an old wooden ship. All that remained in sight of her was her stern post, her name-plate, marked *Plunderer*, a part of her keel, and a few ribs fallen out of place. All these timbers had been blackened by years under the sea. White and blue barnacles were growing on them; sprays of red and white coral had thrust up among them. The sunlight made all these things so glorious suddenly that the Captain turned out the light. Kay could see even the eyes of the lobsters peering into the crannies of the coral.

A mermaid floated to the side of the diving bell. She was young and merry-looking, with bright, big brown eyes and very white teeth. She wore a gold crown over her long brown hair. Her cheeks and lips were full of color. She put her mouth to the glass and smiled at them. "That's Sea-Flower," the Captain said, "Say good morning to her."

"Good morning, Miss Sea-Flower," Kay said. "Can you tell us how this ship came here?"

"Yes," she said. "She was upset in a squall, long ago, and all her men were drowned. They were making merry at the time. You can still see one of them: that scarlet coral is he. But open the door and come with me."

Three other mermaids had swum to the diving bell; together they opened the door. In an instant, Kay was swimming with them in the warm water that was so like green light. All the floor of the sea shone. Here and there were patches of a green plant which had flowers like flames, they were so bright. At first he thought that everything there was dead; but when he had been twenty seconds in that tingling water he knew that it was full of life. The white sand of the sea floor was alive with tiny, scurrying, glittering creatures, little beings looked at him from the branches of the coral, flowers poked out eyes at him upon stalks like snails' horns, he could see the leaves of the seaweeds shine with joy at every good suck-in of light. All these living forms were swaying gently as the swell lifted and fell: all were glistening and tingling with joy; a kind of drowsy song of delight, moved through the water, everything was singing, or murmuring or sighing because life was so good.

Kay went up to a big scarlet fish that had pale goggle-eyes and a collapsing mouth; he tickled its throat; and others knew that he was liking it, because they, too, came to have their throats tickled, till he was surrounded by fish of all colors and shapes, scaled and slimy, finned, or legged, or feelered, all noiseless, most of them strange, many of them most beautiful.

"Come away, Kay," the mermaids said. "But first look at the lovely golden lad."

Lying among the coral, as though he were resting upon a bank of flowers, was a golden image of Saint George, still holding a white shield with a scarlet cross.

"We used to sing to him at first," Sea-Flower said, "hoping that he would wake. The ship was full of golden and silver people at one time. We loved them, they were so very beautiful; but they never answered when we spoke to them. Men came here searching for them in the old days, dragging anchors for them along the sea floor. At last some Indian divers came down and carried them all away to a yacht, all except this one, which they would not touch, because we had so decked it with flowers.

"I see that you know who it was who took those lovely things. He was going to take them to a city of evil men near here. We followed his yacht on his way thither, for we were sad to lose our lovely people. But come, Kay, you shall come with us as far as we can go on the way those golden people went."

They all set out together, Kay between Sea-Flower and Foam-Blossom, each of whom held one of his hands. Foam-Blossom was a golden-haired mermaid, with bright blue eyes and lovely rosy cheeks; she was always laughing. "Is not this lovely?" she said, as they went swimming along.

"O, it is lovely," Kay said. Every stroke of their arms took them over some new kind of shellfish, or past some new anemone or waving weed.

"Come," Sea-Flower said, "let us go in on the tide, at the surface."

They rose up together to the air. There, on the shallow shore, long lines of rollers were always advancing to the beach, toppling as they went and at last shattering. A little river came out to the sea there; its little waves seemed to enjoy meeting the big waves.

"Come," Foam-Blossom said, "let us ride on this big roller that is just going in."

Together, they sat on the neck of the wave, with Kay between them. Kay felt the wave begin to run like a horse, and to gather

66

speed and to lift. Soon the toppling water began to hiss and foam all about them; the shore seemed to rush nearer, and then they all rolled over and over in boiling bubbles into the cool pool of the river, where the seashells looked as though they were all made of pearl.

Soon they were swimming up a river which flowed between ranks of reed and bulrush. Some of the reeds had flowers like the plumes of pampas grass, but pale blue; others had delicate, dangling, yellow tassels. All over these flowers the butterflies were hovering and set-tling. Giant flags grew among the reeds, with heavy blue and white and golden flowers. Little speckled birds with scarlet crests clung to these flowers while they pecked something within them. Water fowl as big as swans, with orange bills and big black and white plumes on their heads, swam to them to be stroked. In the gloom and zebra striping of the light and shade of the reeds Kay saw long-legged water birds standing ankle deep, fishing. Here and there, when they passed mudbanks, he saw the turtles enjoying themselves in the cool ooze.

Presently they left the river and swam up a backwater, where the reeds on both sides gave place to quince trees, which smelled like Arabia from the ripe fruit. At the end of the backwater there was a patch of red mud much poached by the feet of cows that had come to drink there. Beyond the cows was a little roll of grassland.

"The man took the gold and silver things this way," Sea-Flower said. "In those days the river ran this way, through all that grassy piece and for miles beyond it; we often used to swim there. We fol-lowed his yacht for a long way, further than we can see from here. He was a rosy-faced man, not old, but his hair was already gray; his eyes were very bright; and his mouth, when one could see it through the beard, was most cruel and evil. He had three Indians with him, who were his divers and sailors, whom he used to beat.

"When he was in a narrow part of the river, he heard guns, for his city of wickedness was being destroyed. He poled his yacht far into the reeds against the mud, and sent one of his Indians to find out what was happening. As the Indian did not come back, he sent a second Indian; and when the second did not come back he sent a third; but the third did not come back either."

"What happened to the Indians?" Kay asked.

"They all went home to their village in the sea; they have houses there, built upon piles driven into the water. In the rainy seasons they keep very snug in their hammocks and tell each other stories."

"And what happened to Abner Brown, please?"

"He waited for the Indians to bring him news. When they did not come, he changed his yacht's hiding place, by driving her still further into the reeds, and then he set out by himself to find out what was happening. He was captured as a pirate that same night and sent far away.

"Nobody found his boat, she was too well hidden, but there came great changes which hid her further. At first we used to play in the water near her, hoping that she might soon fall to pieces, so that we might have her gold and silver people again; but then there came the earthquake, which raised the river bed and buried the yacht in the mud. After the earthquake there came the summer floods, which made a new channel for the river and altered all the coast. When the floods went down, the place where the yacht lay was five miles from the water and covered deep with flowers, so the birds told us.

"The man came back presently to look for his yacht; but with the land so changed he hardly knew where to begin. We used to see him digging sometimes, when we went up the streams. But he was evil, do not let us think of him; let us go to the sea, to play in the rollers as they burst."

In a few minutes they were on the shining shallow water across which the breaking rollers were marching. At first, Kay was frightened of the waves as they curled and toppled high over his head. Very soon he was wading to meet them, so that they could break all over him or carry him in to the sands.

"And now," the mermaids said, "let us all go down to look at the city under the sea."

They all swam for a few minutes; then Kay suddenly saw something very golden in the green of the underwater.

"Those are the walls," Foam-Blossom said. "And if you listen you will hear the bells. Let us wait here."

They had paused at what had been the harbor. Three or four little ships had sunken with the city; they were there, still secured to the walls. Sponges like big yellow mushrooms covered one; another was starred all over with tiny white shells; another was thickly grown with a weed like many colored ribbons. The walls which had once been of white marble, seemed golden in that dim light. As Kay looked he heard a sweet but muffled booming of the bells as the swell of the water surged and lapsed in the bell tower.

"Come, Kay," Sea-Flower said, "the city gates have fallen open; we can go in."

They passed through the gates, which now drooped upon their hinges from the weight of the shells which grew upon them. Inside the gates was a guard house, with a rack of spears still standing against the wall. Beyond that was a street, with shops open, and fish slowly finning from shop to shop. At the end of the street there was a temple with a bell tower. No one was in that city. Kay went into two of the houses; in one, the kitchen was set out with pots and pans for dinner; two eggs were in a bowl and the bone of a leg of mutton was on a dish; in the other, the beds in the nursery were turned down ready for the children, and in one of the beds a child had set a doll, on which the little shells were growing. There were gaily painted carvings on some of the walls, showing the racing of children and romps and tugs-of-war.

"What is this city, please?" Kay asked. "I would love to go all over it, into every house. What is it called?"

"We call it the Golden City. But look, here come the merchildren playing touch and tag; let us play with them."

At that instant, about twenty little merchildren came darting down the street, at full speed, with streaming hair, bright eyes and laughter. They twisted about like eels, dived down chimneys and through windows, crying aloud from joy in the fun.

"I wonder," Kay said, "if we might play hide and seek? This would be such a lovely place for it."

"Yes," Foam-Blossom said, "let us all play hide and seek; Sea-Flower shall be it. And Kay, you come with me, for I know a lovely place to hide."

She took him through one of the houses into what had been a garden. The fruit trees still stood, but were now crusted over with shells. Sponges, anemones and corals, which were so covered with points of glitter that they seemed full of eyes, grew like mistletoe on the branches. There came a sort of cloud in swift movement across the golden light.

"Look," Foam-Blossom said, "there's a ship passing overhead. If you look up, you may see one of the crew looking down."

"That reminds me," Kay asked, "I meant to ask you before. Did you ever see another man taking away those golden and silver people. He may have taken them away in a big barge."

"Why, Kay," she answered, "that is the *Plunderer* passing. There is the Water Rat Captain looking down. You must be quick; and oh; do look at the flying fish."

Kay felt a sort of swirl as he rushed past a lot of green bubbles into the light. The billows burst all about him suddenly and the sun made him blink. Foam-Blossom, the lovely merchildren, the city and its gardens, among which the beaked fishes had flitted like birds were gone. He was sitting on the end of the *Plunderer's* jib-boom in the clouds of spray flung up as she sailed. Sheets of spray, as bright as snow, soared and flashed all round him. Then he saw that it was not spray, but a flight of flying fish, skimming and falling like darts, all glittering and quivering. "O, how lovely," he cried.

As he cried, he heard his window creak; somebody rolled him into bed and the *Plunderer* went back to the wall. As for the sea, it was not there. When he opened his eyes, Ellen was there, but no water at all.

The Old Man
of Cury

ROBERT HUNT

ORE than a hundred years since, on a fine summer day, when the sun shone brilliantly from a cloudless sky, an old man from the parish of Cury, or, as it was called in olden times, Corantyn, was walking on the sands in one of the coves near the Lizard Point. The old man was meditating, or at least he was walking onward, either thinking deeply, or not thinking at all—that is, he was "lost in thought" —when suddenly he came upon a rock on which was sitting a beautiful girl with fair hair, so long that it covered her entire person. On the in-shore side of the rock was a pool of the most transparent water, which had been left by the receding tide in the sandy hollow the waters had scooped out. This young creature was so absorbed in her occupation, arranging her hair in the watery mirror, or in admiration of her own lovely face, that she was unconscious of an intruder.

The old man stood looking at her for some time ere he made up his mind how to act. At length he resolved to speak to the maiden. "What cheer, young one?" he said, "What art thee doing there by thyself, then, this time o'day?"

As soon as she heard the voice, she slid off the rock entirely under the water. The old man could not tell what to make of it. He thought the girl would drown herself, so he ran on to the rock to render her assistance, conceiving that in her fright at being found naked by a man she had fallen into the pool, and possibly it was deep enough to drown her. He looked into the water, and, sure enough, he could make out the head and shoulders of a woman, and long hair floating like fine seaweeds all over the pond, hiding what appeared to him to be a fish's tail. He could not, however, see anything distinctly owing to the abundance of hair floating around the figure. The old man had heard of mermaids from the fishermen of Gunwalloe; so he conceived this lady must be one, and he was at first very much frightened. He saw that the young lady was quite as much terrified as he was, and that, from shame or fear, she endeavored to hide herself in the crevices of the rock, and bury herself under the seaweeds.

Summoning courage, at last the old man addressed her, "Don't be afraid, my dear. You needn't mind me. I wouldn't do ye any harm. I'm an old man, and wouldn't hurt ye any more than your grandfather."

After he had talked in this soothing strain for some time, the young lady took courage, and raised her head above the water. She was crying bitterly, and, as soon as she could speak, she begged the old man to go away.

"I must know, my dearie, something about ye, now I have caught ye. It is not every day that an old man catches a merry-maid, and I have heard some strange tales of you water-ladies. Now, my dear, don't be afraid, I would not hurt a single hair of that beautiful head. How came ye here?" After some further coaxing she told the old man the following story.

She and her husband and little ones had been busy at sea all morning, and they were very tired with swimming in the hot sun; so the merman proposed that they should retire to a cavern, which they were in the habit of visiting in Kynance Cove. Away they all swam, and entered the cavern at mid-tide. As there was some nice soft weed, and the cave was deliciously cool, the merman was disposed to sleep and told them not to wake him until the rise of the tide. He was soon fast alseep, snoring most lustily. The children crept out and were playing on the lovely sands; so the mermaid thought she should like to look at the world a little. She looked with delight on the children rolling to and fro in the shallow waves, and she laughed heartily at the crabs fighting in their own funny way.

"The scent from the flowers came down over the cliffs so sweetly," said she, "that I longed to get nearer the lovely things which yielded those rich odors, and I floated on from rock to rock until I came to this one; and finding that I could not proceed any further, I thought I would seize the opportunity of dressing my hair." She passed her fingers through those beautiful locks, and shook out a number of small crabs and much broken seaweed. She went on to say that she had sat on the rock amusing herself, until the voice of a mortal terrified her, and until then she had no idea that the sea was so far out, and a long dry bar of sand between her and it. "What shall I do! what shall I do? Oh! I'd give the world to get out to sea! Oh! oh! what shall I do?"

The old man endeavored to console her, but his attempts were in vain. She told him her husband would "carry on" most dreadfully if he awoke and found her absent, and he would be certain of awaking at the turn of the tide, as that was his dinner time. He was very savage when he was hungry, and would as soon eat the children as not, if there was no other food at hand. He was also dreadfully jealous, and if she was not at his side when he awoke, he would at once suspect her of having run off with some other merman.

She begged the old man to bear her out to sea. If he would but do so, she would procure him any three things he would wish for. Her entreaties at length prevailed; and, according to her desire, the old man knelt down on the rock with his back towards her. She clasped her fair arms around his neck, and locked her long finny fingers together on his throat. He got up from the rock with his burden, and carried the mermaid thus across the sands. As she rode in this way, she asked the old man to tell her what he desired.

"I will not wish," said he, "for silver and gold, but give me the power to do good to my neighbors: first, to break the spells of witch-craft; next to charm away diseases; and thirdly, to discover thieves, and restore stolen goods."

All this she promised he should possess; but he must come to a half-tide rock on another day, and she would instruct him how to accomplish the three things he desired. They had reached the water, and taking her comb from her hair, she gave it to the old man, telling him he had but to comb the water and call her at any time, and she would come to him. The mermaid loosened her grasp, and sliding off the old man's back into the sea, she waved him a kiss and disappeared.

At the appointed time the old man was at the rock—known to the present time as the Mermaid's Rock, and duly was he instructed in many mysteries. Among others, he learned to break the spells of witches from man or beast; to prepare a vessel of water, in which to show to anyone who had property stolen the face of the thief; to charm shingles, tetters, St. Anthony's fire, and St. Vitus's dance; and he learned also all the mysteries of bramble leaves and the like.

The mermaid had a woman's curiosity, and she persuaded her old friend to take her to some secret place, from which she could see more of the dry land, and of the funny people who lived on it, who had their tails split, so that they could walk. On taking the mermaid back to the sea, she wished her friend to visit her abode, and promised even to make him young if he would do so, which favor the old gentleman respectfully declined.

A family well known in Cornwall have for some generations exercised the power of charming, etc. They account for the possession of this power in the manner related. It was some remote great-grandfather of theirs who received the mermaid's comb, which they retain to the present day, and show as evidence of the truth of their being supernaturally endowed. Some people are unbelieving enough to say the comb is only a part of a shark's jaw. Skeptical people are never lovable people.

<center>~~~~~~ 🌼 ~~~~~~</center>

The Mermaid of Lighthouse Point

BRET HARTE

SOME forty years ago, on the northern coast of California, near the Golden Gate, stood a lighthouse. Of a primitive class, since superseded by a building more in keeping with the growing magnitude of the adjacent port, it attracted little attention from the desolate shore, and, it was alleged, still less from the desolate sea beyond. A gray structure of timber, stone, and glass, it was buffeted and harried by the constant trade winds, baked by the unclouded six months' sun, lost for a few hours in the afternoon sea-fog, and laughed over by circling

75

guillemots from the Farallones.

It was kept by a recluse—a preoccupied man of scientific tastes, who, in shameless contrast to his fellow immigrants, had applied to the government for this scarcely lucrative position as a means of securing the seclusion he valued more than gold. Some believed that he was the victim of an early disappointment in love—a view charitably taken by those who also believed that the government would not have appointed "a crank" to a position of responsibility. Howbeit, he fulfilled his duties, and, with the assistance of an Indian, even cultivated a small patch of ground beside the lighthouse.

His isolation was complete! There was little to attract wanderers here: the nearest mines were fifty miles away; the virgin forest on the mountains inland were penetrated only by sawmills and wood-men from the Bay settlements, equally remote. Although by the shore-line the lights of the great port were sometimes plainly visible, yet the solitude around him was peopled only by Indians—a branch of the great northern tribe of "root-diggers,"—peaceful and simple in their habits, as yet undisturbed by the white man, nor stirred into antagonism by aggression. Civilization only touched him at stated intervals, and then by the more expeditious sea from the government boat that brought him supplies. But for his contiguity to the per-petual turmoil of wind and sea, he might have passed a restful Arcadian life in his surroundings; for even his solitude was some-times haunted by this faint reminder of the great port hard by that pulsated with an equal unrest. Nevertheless, the sands before his door and the rocks behind him seemed to have been untrodden by any other white man's foot since their upheaval from the ocean.

It was true that the little bay beside him was marked on the map as "Sir Francis Drake's Bay," tradition having located it as the spot where that ingenious pirate and empire-maker had once landed his vessels and scraped the barnacles from his adventurous keels. But of this Edgar Pomfrey—or "Captain Pomfrey," as he was called by virtue of his half-nautical office—had thought little.

For the first six months he had thoroughly enjoyed his seclusion. In the company of his books, of which he had brought such a fair store that their shelves lined his snug corners to the exclusion of more comfortable furniture, he found his principal recreation. Even his unwonted manual labor, the trimming of his lamp and cleaning of his reflectors, and his personal housekeeping, in which his Indian help at times assisted, he found a novel and interesting occupation. For outdoor exercise, a ramble on the sands, a climb to the rocky upland, or a pull in the lighthouse boat, amply sufficed him.

"Crank" as he was supposed to be, he was sane enough to guard against any of those early lapses into barbarism which marked the lives of some solitary gold-miners. His own taste, as well as the duty of his office, kept his person and habitation sweet and clean, and his habits regular. Even the little cultivated patch of ground on the lee side of the tower was symmetrical and well ordered. Thus the outward light of Captain Pomfrey shone forth over the wilderness of shore and wave, even like his beacon, whatever his inward illumination may have been.

It was a bright summer morning, remarkable even in the monotonous excellence of the season, with a slight touch of warmth which the invincible Northwest Trades had not yet chilled. There was still a faint haze off the coast, as if last night's fog had been caught in the quick sunshine, and the shining sands were hot, but without the usual dazzling glare. A faint perfume from a quaint lilac-colored beach flower, whose clustering heads dotted the sand like bits of blown spume, took the place of that smell of the sea which the odorless Pacific lacked. A few rocks, half a mile away, lifted themselves above the ebb tide at varying heights as they lay on the trough of the swell, were crested with foam by a striking surge, or cleanly erased in the full sweep of the sea. Beside, and partly upon one of the higher rocks, a singular object was moving.

Pomfrey was interested but not startled. He had once or twice seen seals disporting on these rocks, and on one occasion a sea lion,—an estray from the familiar rocks on the other side of the Golden Gate. But he ceased work in his garden patch, and coming to his house, exchanged his hoe for a telescope.

When he got the mystery in focus he suddenly stopped and

rubbed the object-glass with his handkerchief. But even when he applied the glass to his eye for a second time, he could scarcely believe his eyesight. For the object seemed to be a *woman*, the lower part of her figure submerged in the sea, her long hair depending over her shoulders and waist. There was nothing in her attitude to suggest terror or that she was the victim of some accident. She moved slowly and complacently with the sea, and even—a more staggering suggestion—appeared to be combing out the strands of her long hair with her fingers. With her body half concealed she might have been a mermaid!

He swept the foreshore and horizon with his glass; there was neither boat nor ship—nor anything that moved, except the long swell of the Pacific. She could have come only from the sea; for to reach the rocks by land she would have had to pass before the lighthouse, while the narrow strip of shore which curved northward beyond his range of view he knew was inhabited only by Indians. But the woman was unhesitatingly and appallingly *white*, and her hair light even to a golden gleam in the sunshine.

Pomfrey was a gentleman, and as such was amazed, dismayed, and cruelly embarrassed. If she was a simple bather from some vicinity hitherto unknown and unsuspected by him, it was clearly his business to shut up his glass and go back to his garden patch—although the propinquity of himself and the lighthouse must have been as plainly visible to her as she was to him. On the other hand, if she was the survivor of some wreck and in distress—or, as he even fancied from her reckless manner, bereft of her senses, his duty to rescue her was equally clear.

In his dilemma he determined upon a compromise and ran to his boat. He would pull out to sea, pass between the rocks and the curving sand-spit, and examine the sands and sea more closely for signs of wreckage, or some overlooked waiting boat near the shore. He would be within hail if she needed him, or she could escape to her boat if she had one.

In another moment his boat was lifting on the swell towards the rocks. He pulled quickly, occasionally turning to note that the strange

78

figure, whose movements were quite discernible to the naked eye, was still there, but gazing more earnestly towards the nearest shore for any sign of life or occupation. In ten minutes he had reached the curve where the trend opened northward, and the long line of shore stretched before him.

He swept it eagerly with a single searching glance. Sea and shore were empty. He turned quickly to the rock, scarcely a hundred yards on his beam. It was empty too! Forgetting his previous scruples, he pulled directly for it until his keel grated on its submerged base. There was nothing there but the rock, slippery with the yellow-green slime of seaweed and kelp—neither trace nor sign of the figure that had occupied it a moment ago. He pulled around it; there was no cleft or hiding place. For an instant his heart leaped at the sight of something white, caught in a jagged tooth of the outlying reef, but it was only the bleached fragment of a bamboo orange crate, cast from the deck of some South Sea trader, such as often strewed the beach. He lay off the rock, keeping way in the swell, and scrutinizing the glittering sea. At last he pulled back to the lighthouse, perplexed and discomfited.

Was it simply a sporting seal, transformed by some trick of his vision? But he had seen it through his glass, and now remembered such details as the face and features framed in their contour of golden hair, and believed he could even have identified them. He examined the rock again with his glass, and was surprised to see how clearly it was outlined now in its barren loneliness. Yet he must have been mistaken. His scientific and accurate mind allowed of no errant fancy, and he had always sneered at the marvelous as the result of hasty or superficial observation. He was a little worried at this lapse of his healthy accuracy,—fearing that it might be the result of his seclusion and loneliness,—akin to the visions of the recluse and solitary. It was strange, too, that it should take the shape of a woman; for Edgar Pomfrey had a story—the usual old and foolish one.

Then his thoughts took a lighter phase, and he turned to the memory of his books, and finally to the books themselves. From a shelf he picked out a volume of old voyages, and turned to a remembered passage: "In other seas doe abound marvells soche as Sea Spyders of the bigness of a pinnace, the wich they have been known to attack and destroy; Sea Vypers which reach to the top of a goodly maste, whereby they are able to draw marinners from the rigging by the suction of their breathes; and Devill Fyshe, which vomit fire by night which makyth the sea to shine prodigiously, and mermaydes. They are half fyshe and half mayde of grate Beauty, and have been seen of divers godly and creditable witnesses swymming beside rocks, hidden to their waist in the sea, combing of their hayres, to the help of whych they carry a small mirrore of the bigness of their fingers." Pomfrey laid the book aside with a faint smile. To even this credulity he might come!

Nevertheless, he used the telescope again that day. But there was no repetition of the incident, and he was forced to believe that he had been the victim of some extraordinary illusion.

The next morning, however, with his calmer judgment doubts began to visit him. There was no one of whom he could make inquiries but his Indian helper, and their conversation had usually been restricted to the language of signs or the use of a few words he had picked up. He contrived, however, to ask if there was a "waugee" (white) woman in the neighborhood. The Indian shook his head in surprise. There was no "waugee" nearer than the remote mountain ridge to which he pointed. Pomfrey was obliged to be content with this. Even had his vocabulary been larger, he would as soon have thought of revealing the embarrassing secret of this woman, whom he believed to be of his own race, to a mere barbarian as he would of asking him to verify his own impressions by allowing him to look at her that morning. The next day, however, something happened which forced him to resume his inquiries.

He was rowing around the curving spot when he saw a number of black objects on the northern sands moving in and out of the surf, which he presently made out as Indians. A nearer approach satisfied him that they were wading squaws and children gathering seaweed and shells. He would have pushed his acquaintance still nearer, but as his boat rounded the point, with one accord they all scuttled away like frightened sandpipers. Pomfrey, on his return, asked his Indian retainer if they could swim. "Oh, yes!" "As far as the rock?" "Yes." Yet Pomfrey was not satisfied. The color of his strange apparition remained unaccounted for, and it was not that of an Indian woman.

Trifling events linger long in a monotonous existence, and it was nearly a week before Pomfrey gave up his daily telescopic inspection of the rock. Then he fell back upon his books again, and, oddly enough, upon another volume of voyages, and so chanced upon the account of Sir Francis Drake's occupation of the bay before him. He had always thought it strange that the great adventurer had left no trace or sign of his sojourn there; still stranger that he should have overlooked the presence of gold, known even to the Indians themselves, and have lost a discovery far beyond his wildest dreams and a treasure to which the cargoes of those Philippine galleons he had more or less successfully intercepted were trifles. Had the restless explorer been content to pace those dreary sands during three weeks of inactivity, with no thought of penetrating the inland forests behind the range, or of even entering the nobler bay beyond? Or was the location of the spot a mere tradition as wild and unsupported as the "marvells" of the other volume? Pomfrey had the skepticism of the scientific, inquiring mind.

Two weeks had passed and he was returning from a long climb inland, when he stopped to rest in his descent to the sea. The panorama of the shore was before him, from its uttermost limit to the lighthouse on the northern point. The sun was still one hour high, it would take him about that time to reach home. But from this coign of vantage he could see—what he had not before observed—that what he had always believed was a little cove on the northern shore was really the estuary of a small stream which rose near him and eventually descended into the ocean at that point. He could also see that beside it was a long low erection of some kind, covered with thatched brush, which looked like a "barrow," yet showed signs of habitation in the slight smoke that rose from it and drifted inland.

It was not far out of his way, and he resolved to return in that direction. On his way down he once or twice heard the barking of an Indian dog, and knew that he must be in the vicinity of an encampment. A campfire, with the ashes yet warm, proved that he was on the trail of one of the nomadic tribes, but the declining sun warned him to hasten home to his duty. When he at last reached the estuary, he found that the building beside it was little else than a long hut, whose thatched and mud-plastered mound-like roof gave it the appearance of a cave. Its single opening and entrance abutted on the water's edge, and the smoke he had noticed rolled through this entrance from a smouldering fire within.

Pomfrey had little difficulty in recognizing the purpose of this strange structure from the accounts he had heard from "loggers" of the Indian customs. The cave was a "sweat-house"—a calorific chamber in which the Indians closely shut themselves, naked, with a "smudge" or smouldering fire of leaves, until, perspiring and half suffocated, they rushed from the entrance and threw themselves into the water before it. The still smouldering fire told him that the house had been used that morning, and he made no doubt that the Indians were encamped nearby. He would have liked to pursue his researches further, but he found he had already trespassed upon his remaining time, and he turned somewhat abruptly away—so abruptly, in fact, that a figure, which had evidently been cautiously following him at a distance, had no time to get away. His heart leaped with astonishment.

It was the woman he had seen on the rock.

Although her native dress now only disclosed her head and hands, there was no doubt about her color, and it was distinctly white, save for the tanning of exposure and a slight red ochre marking on her low forehead. And her hair, long and unkempt as it was, showed that he had not erred in his first impression of it. It was a tawny flaxen, with fainter bleachings where the sun had touched it most. Her eyes were of a clear Northern blue. Her dress, which was quite distinctive in that it was neither the cast off finery of civilization nor the cheap "government" flannels and calicos usually worn by the Californian tribes, was purely native, and of fringed deerskin, and consisted of a long, loose shirt and leggings worked with bright feathers and colored shells. A necklace, also of shells and fancy pebbles, hung round her neck. She seemed to be a fully developed woman, in spite of the girlishness of her flowing hair, and notwithstanding the shapeless length of her gaberdine-like garment, taller than the ordinary squaw.

Pomfrey saw all this in a single flash of perception, for the next instant she was gone, disappearing behind the sweat-house. He ran after her, catching sight of her again, half doubled up, in the characteristic Indian trot, dodging around rocks and low bushes as she fled along the banks of the stream. But for her distinguishing hair, she looked in her flight like an ordinary frightened squaw. This, which gave a sense of unmanliness and ridicule to his own pursuit of her, with the fact that his hour of duty was drawing near and he was still far from the lighthouse, checked him in full career, and he turned regretfully away. He had called after her at first, and she had not heeded him. What he would have said to her he did not know.

He hastened home, discomfited, even embarrassed—yet excited to a degree he had not deemed possible in himself.

During the morning his thoughts were full of her. Theory after theory for her strange existence there he examined and dismissed. His first thought, that she was a white woman—some settler's wife—masquerading in Indian garb, he abandoned when he saw her moving; no white woman could imitate that Indian trot, nor would remember to attempt it if she were frightened. The idea that she was a captive white, held by the Indians, became ridiculous when he thought of the nearness of civilization and the peaceful, timid character of the "digger" tribes. That she was some unfortunate demented creature who had escaped from her keeper and wandered into the wilderness, a glance at her clear, frank, intelligent, curious eyes had contradicted. There was but one theory left—the most sensible and practical one—that she was the offspring of some white man and Indian squaw. Yet this he found, oddly enough, the least palatable to his fancy. And the few half-breeds he had seen were not at all like her.

The next morning he had recourse to his Indian retainer, "Jim."

With infinite difficulty, protraction, and not a little embarrassment, he finally made him understand that he had seen a "white squaw" near the "sweat-house," and that he wanted to know more about her. With equal difficulty Jim finally recognized the fact of the existence of such a person, but immediately afterwards shook his head in an emphatic negation. With greater difficulty and greater mortification Pomfrey presently ascertained that Jim's negative referred to a supposed abduction of the woman which he understood that his employer seriously contemplated.

But he also learned that she was a real Indian, and that there were three or four others like her, male and female, in that vicinity; that from a "skeena mowitch" (little baby) they were all like that, and that their parents were of the same color, but never a white or "waugee" man or woman among them; that they were looked upon as a distinct and superior caste of Indians, and enjoyed certain privileges with the tribe; that they superstitiously avoided white men, of whom they had the greatest fear, and that they were protected in this by the other Indians; that it was marvelous and almost beyond belief that Pomfrey had been able to see one, for no other white man had, or was even aware of their existence.

How much of this he actually understood, how much of it was lying and due to Jim's belief that he wished to abduct the fair stranger, Pomfrey was unable to determine. There was enough, however, to excite his curiosity strongly and occupy his mind to the exclusion of his books—save one.

Among his smaller volumes he had found a travel book of the "Chinook Jargon," with a lexicon of many of the words commonly used by the Northern Pacific tribes. An hour or two's trial with the astonished Jim gave him an increased vocabulary and a new occupation. Each day the incongruous pair took a lesson from the lexicon. In a week Pomfrey felt he would be able to accost the mysterious stranger. But he did not again surprise her in any of his rambles, or even in a later visit to the sweat-house. He had learned from Jim that the house was only used by the "bucks," or males, and that her appearance there had been accidental. He recalled that he had had the impression that she had been stealthily following him, and the recollection gave him a pleasure he could not account for. But an incident presently occurred which gave him a new idea of her relations towards him.

The difficulty of making Jim understand had hitherto prevented Pomfrey from intrusting him with the care of the lantern; but with the aid of the lexicon he had been able to make him comprehend its working, and under Pomfrey's personal guidance the Indian had once or twice lit the lamp and set its machinery in motion.

It remained for him only to test Jim's unaided capacity, in case of his own absence or illness. It happened to be a warm, beautiful sunset, when the afternoon fog had for once delayed its invasion of the shoreline, that he left the lighthouse to Jim's undivided care, and reclining on a sand dune still warm from the sun, lazily watched the result of Jim's first essay. As the twilight deepened, and the first flash of the lantern strove with the dying glories of the sun, Pomfrey presently became aware that he was not the only watcher.

A little gray figure creeping on all fours suddenly glided out of the shadow of another sand dune and then halted, falling back on its knees, gazing fixedly at the growing light. It was the woman he had seen. She was not a dozen yards away, and in her eagerness and utter absorption in the light had evidently overlooked him. He could see her face distinctly, her lips parted half in wonder, half with the breathless absorption of a devotee.

A faint sense of disappointment came over him. It was not *him* she was watching, but the light! As it swelled out over the darkening gray sand she turned as if to watch its effect around her, and caught sight of Pomfrey. With a little startled cry—the first she had uttered —she darted away. He did not follow. A moment before, when he first saw her, an Indian salutation which he had learned from Jim had risen to his lips, but in the odd feeling which her fascination of the light had caused him he had not spoken. He watched her bent figure scuttling away like some frightened animal, with a critical consciousness that she was really scarce human, and went back to the lighthouse. He would not run after her again! Yet that evening

85

he continued to think of her, and recalled her voice, which struck him now as having been at once melodious and childlike, and wished he had at least spoken, and perhaps elicited a reply.

He did not, however, haunt the sweat-house near the river again. Yet he still continued his lessons with Jim, and in this way, perhaps, although quite unpremeditatedly, enlisted a humble ally. A week passed in which he had not alluded to her, when one morning, as he was returning from a row, Jim met him mysteriously on the beach.

"S'pose him come slow, slow," said Jim gravely, airing his newly acquired English; "make no noise—plenty catchee Indian maiden." The last epithet was the polite lexicon equivalent of squaw.

Pomfrey, not entirely satisfied in his mind, nevertheless softly followed the noiselessly gliding Jim to the lighthouse. Here Jim cautiously opened the door, motioning Pomfrey to enter.

The base of the tower was composed of two living rooms, a store-room and oil tank. As Pomfrey entered, Jim closed the door softly behind him. The abrupt transition from the glare of the sands and sun to the semi-darkness of the storeroom at first prevented him from seeing anything, but he was instantly distracted by a scurrying flutter and wild beating of the walls, as of a caged bird.

In another moment he could make out the fair stranger, quivering with excitement, passionately dashing at the barred window, the walls, the locked door, and circling around the room in her desperate attempt to find an egress, like a captured seagull. Amazed, mystified, indignant with Jim, himself, and even his unfortunate captive, Pomfrey called to her in Chinook to stop, and going to the door, flung it wide open.

She darted by him, raising her soft blue eyes for an instant in a swift, sidelong glance of half appeal, half-frightened admiration, and rushed out into the open. But here, to his surprise, she did not run away. On the contrary, she drew herself up with a dignity that seemed to increase her height, and walked majestically towards Jim, who at her unexpected exit had suddenly thrown himself upon the sand, in utterly abject terror and supplication. She approached him slowly, with one small hand uplifted in a menacing gesture. The man writhed and squirmed before her. Then she turned, caught sight of Pomfrey standing in the doorway, and walked quietly away.

Amazed, yet gratified with this new assertion of herself, Pomfrey respectfully, but alas! incautiously, called after her. In an instant, at the sound of his voice, she dropped again into her slouching Indian trot and glided away over the sandhills.

Pomfrey did not add any reproof of his own to the discomfiture of his Indian retainer. Neither did he attempt to inquire the secret of this savage girl's power over him. It was evident he had spoken truly when he told his master that she was of a superior caste. Pomfrey recalled her erect and indignant figure standing over the prostrate Jim, and was again perplexed and disappointed at her sudden lapse into the timid savage at the sound of his voice. Would not this well-meant but miserable trick of Jim's have the effect of increasing her unreasoning animal-like distrust of him? A few days later brought an unexpected answer to his question.

It was the hottest hour of the day. He had been fishing off the reef of rocks where he had first seen her, and had taken in his line and was leisurely pulling for the lighthouse.

Suddenly a little musical cry not unlike a bird's struck his ear. He lay on his oars and listened. It was repeated; but this time it was unmistakably recognizable as the voice of the Indian girl, although he had heard it but once.

He turned eagerly to the rock, but it was empty; he pulled around it, but saw nothing. He looked towards the shore, and swung his boat in that direction, when again the cry was repeated with the faintest quaver of a laugh, apparently on the level of the sea before him. For the first time he looked down, and there on the crest of a wave not a dozen yards ahead, danced the yellow hair and laughing eyes of the girl. The frightened gravity of her look was gone, lost in the flash of her white teeth and quivering dimples as her dripping face rose above the sea. When their eyes met she dived again, but quickly reappeared on the other bow, swimming with lazy, easy strokes, her smiling head thrown back over her white shoulder, as if luring him to a race. If her smile was a revelation to him, still more so was this first touch of feminine coquetry in her attitude.

He pulled eagerly towards her; with a few long overhand strokes she kept her distance, or, if he approached too near, she dived like a loon, coming up astern of him with the same childlike, mocking cry. In vain he pursued her, calling her to stop in her own tongue, and laughingly protested; she easily avoided his boat at every turn. Suddenly, when they were nearly abreast of the river estuary, she rose in the water, and, waving her little hands with a gesture of farewell, turned, and curving her back like a dolphin, leaped into the surging swell of the estuary bar and was lost in its foam.

It would have been madness for him to have attempted to follow in his boat, and he saw that she knew it. He waited until her yellow crest appeared in the smoother water of the river, and then rowed back. In his excitement and preoccupation he had quite forgotten his long exposure to the sun during his active exercise, and that he was poorly equipped for the cold sea fog which the heat had brought in earlier, and which now was quietly obliterating sea and shore. This made his progress slower and more difficult, and by the time he had reached the lighthouse he was chilled to the bone.

The next morning he woke with a dull headache and great weariness, and it was with considerable difficulty that he could attend to his duties. At nightfall, feeling worse, he determined to transfer the care of the light to Jim, but was amazed to find that he had disappeared, and what was more ominous, a bottle of spirits which Pomfrey had taken from his locker the night before had disappeared too. Jim evidently had been tempted, had fallen, and was too ashamed or too drunk to face his master.

Pomfrey, however, managed to get the light in order and working, and then, he scarcely knew how, betook himself to bed in a state of high fever. He turned from side to side racked by pain, with burning lips and pulses. Strange fancies beset him; he had noticed when he lit his light that a strange sail was looming off the estuary—a place where no sail had ever been seen or should be—and was relieved that the lighting of the tower might show the reckless or ignorant mariner his real bearings for the "Gate." At times he had heard voices above the familiar song of the surf, and tried to rise from his bed, but could not. Sometimes these voices were strange, outlandish, dissonant, in his own language, yet only partly intelligible; but through them always rang a single voice, musical, familiar, yet of a tongue not his own—hers!

And then, out of his delirium—for such it proved afterwards to be —came a strange vision. He thought that he had just lit the light when, from some strange and unaccountable reason, it suddenly became dim and defied all his efforts to revive it. To add to his discomfiture, he could see quite plainly through the lantern a strange-looking vessel standing in from the sea. She was so clearly out of her course for the Gate that he knew she had not seen the light, and his limbs trembled with shame and terror as he tried in vain to rekindle the dying light. Yet to his surprise the strange ship kept steadily on, passing the dangerous reef of rocks, until she was actually in the waters of the bay. But stranger than all, swimming beneath her bows was the golden head and laughing face of the Indian girl, even as he had seen it the day before. A revulsion of feeling overtook him. Believing that she was luring the ship to its destruction, he ran out on the beach and strove to hail the vessel and warn it of its impending doom. But he could not speak—no sound came from his lips. And now his attention was absorbed by the ship itself.

High-bowed and pooped, and curved like the crescent moon, it was the strangest craft that he had ever seen. Even as he gazed it glided on nearer and nearer, and at last beached itself noiselessly on the sands before his own feet. A score of figures as bizarre and outlandish as the ship itself now thronged its high forecastle—really a castle in shape and warlike purpose—and leaped from its ports. The common seamen were nearly naked to the waist; the officers looked more like soldiers than sailors. What struck him more strangely was that they were one and all seemingly unconscious of the existence of the lighthouse, sauntering up and down carelessly, as if on some uninhabited strand, and even talking—so far as he could understand their old bookish dialect—as if in some hitherto undiscovered land.

Their ignorance of the geography of the whole coast, and even of the sea from which they came, actually aroused his critical indignation; their coarse and stupid allusions to the fair Indian swimmer as the "mermaid" that they had seen upon their bow made him more furious still. Yet he was helpless to express his contemptuous anger, or even make them conscious of his presence. Then an interval of incoherency and utter blankness followed.

When he again took up the thread of his fancy the ship seemed to be lying on her beam ends on the sand; the strange arrangement of her upper deck and top-hamper, more like a dwelling than any ship he had ever seen, was fully exposed to view, while the seamen seemed to be at work with the rudest contrivances, calking and scraping her barnacled sides. He saw that phantom crew, when not working, at wassail, and festivity; heard the shouts of drunken roisterers; saw the placing of a guard around some of the most uncontrollable, and later detected the stealthy escape of half a dozen sailors inland, amidst the fruitless volley fired upon them from obsolete blunderbusses. Then his vision transported him inland, where he saw these seamen following some Indian women. Suddenly one of them turned and ran frenziedly towards him as if seeking succor, closely pursued by one of the sailors. Pomfrey strove to reach her, struggled violently with the fearful apathy that seemed to hold his limbs, and then, as she uttered at last a little musical cry, burst his bonds and—awoke!

As consciousness slowly struggled back to him, he could see the bare wooden-like walls of his sleeping room, the locker, the one window bright with sunlight, the open door of the tank room, and the little staircase to the tower. There was a smoky and herb-like smell in the room. He made an effort to rise, but as he did so a small sunburnt hand was laid gently yet restrainingly upon his shoulder, and he heard the same musical cry as before, but this time modulated to a girlish laugh. He raised his head faintly. Half squatting, half kneeling by his bed was the yellow-haired stranger.

With the recollection of his vision still perplexing him, he said in a weak voice, "Who are you?"

Her blue eyes met his own with quick intelligence and no trace of her former timidity. A soft, caressing light had taken its place. Pointing with her finger to her breast in a childlike gesture, she said, "Me—Olooya."

"Olooya!" He remembered suddenly that Jim had always used that word in speaking of her, but until then he had always thought it was some Indian term for her distinct class.

"Olooya," he repeated. Then, with difficulty attempting to use her own tongue, he asked, "When did you come here?"

"Last night," she answered in the same tongue. "There was no witch-fire there," she continued, pointing to the tower; "when it came not, Olooya came! Olooya found white chief sick and alone. White chief could not get up! Olooya lit witch-fire for him."

"You?" he repeated in astonishment. "I lit it myself."

She looked at him pityingly, as if still recognizing his delirium, and shook her head. "White chief was sick—how can know? Olooya made witch-fire."

He cast a hurried glance at his watch hanging on the wall beside him. It had *run down*, although he had wound it the last thing before going to bed. He had evidently been lying there helpless beyond the twenty-four hours!

He groaned and turned to rise, but she gently forced him down again, and gave him some herbal infusion, in which he recognized the taste of the Yerba Buena vine which grew by the river. Then she made him comprehend in her own tongue that Jim had been decoyed, while drunk, aboard a certain schooner lying off the shore at a spot where she had seen some men digging in the sands. She had not gone there, for she was afraid of the bad men, and a slight return of her former terror came into her changeful eyes. She knew how to light the witch-light; she reminded him she had been in the tower before.

"You have saved my light, and perhaps my life," he said weakly, taking her hand.

Possibly she did not understand him, for her only answer was a vague smile. But the next instant she started up, listening intently,

91

and then with a frightened cry drew away her hand and suddenly dashed out of the building. In the midst of his amazement the door was darkened by a figure—a stranger dressed like an ordinary miner. Pausing a moment to look after the flying Olooya, the man turned and glanced around the room, and then with a coarse, familiar smile approached Pomfrey.

"Hope I ain't disturbin' ye, but I allowed I'd just be neighborly and drop in—seein' as this is govnment property, and me and my pardners, as American citizens and taxpayers, helps to support it. We're coastin' from Trinidad down here and prospectin' along the beach for gold in the sand. Ye seem to hev a mighty soft berth of it here—nothing to do—and lots of purty half-breeds hangin' round!"

The man's effrontery was too much for Pomfrey's self-control, weakened by illness. "It *is* government property," he answered hotly, "and you have no more right to intrude upon it than you have to decoy away my servant, a government employee, during my illness, and jeopardize that property."

The unexpectedness of this attack, and the sudden revelation of the fact of Pomfrey's illness in his flushed face and hollow voice apparently frightened and confused the stranger. He stammered a surly excuse, backed out of the doorway, and disappeared. An hour later Jim appeared, crestfallen, remorseful, and extravagantly penitent. Pomfrey was too weak for reproaches or inquiry, and he was thinking only of Olooya.

She did not return. His recovery in that keen air, aided, as he sometimes thought, by the herbs she had given him, was almost as rapid as his illness. The miners did not again intrude upon the lighthouse nor trouble his seclusion. When he was able to sun himself on the sands, he could see them in the distance at work on the beach. He reflected that she would not come back while they were there, and was reconciled. But one morning Jim appeared, awkward and embarrassed, leading another Indian, whom he introduced as Olooya's brother. Pomfrey's suspicions were aroused. Except that the stranger had something of the girl's superiority of manner, there was no likeness whatever to his fair-haired acquaintance.

But a fury of indignation was added to his suspicions when he learned the amazing purport of their visit. It was nothing less than an offer from the alleged brother to *sell* his sister to Pomfrey for forty dollars and a jug of whiskey! Unfortunately, Pomfrey's temper once more got the better of his judgment. With a scathing exposition of the laws under which the Indian and white man equally lived, and the legal punishment of kidnaping, he swept what he believed was the imposter from his presence. He was scarcely alone again before he remembered that his imprudence might affect the girl's future access to him, but it was too late now.

Still he clung to the belief that he should see her when the prospectors had departed, and he hailed with delight the breaking up of the camp near the "sweat-house" and the disappearance of the schooner. It seemed that their gold-seeking was unsuccessful; but Pomfrey was struck, on visiting the locality, to find that in their excavations in the sand at the estuary they had uncovered the decaying timbers of a ship's small boat of some ancient and obsolete construction. This made him think of his strange dream, with a vague sense of warning which he could not shake off, and on his return to the lighthouse he took from his shelves a copy of the old voyages to see how far his fancy had been affected by his reading.

In the account of Drake's visit to the coast he found a footnote which he had overlooked before, and which ran as follows: "The Admiral seems to have lost several of his crew by desertion, who were supposed to have perished miserably by starvation in the inhospitable interior or by the hands of savages. But later voyagers have suggested that the deserters married Indian wives, and there is a legend that a hundred years later a singular race of half-breeds, bearing unmistakable Anglo-Saxon characteristics, was found in that locality." Pomfrey fell into a reverie of strange hypotheses and fancies. He resolved that, when he again saw Olooya, he would question her; her terror of these men might be simply racial or some hereditary transmission.

But his intention was never fulfilled. For when days and weeks had elapsed, and he had vainly haunted the river estuary and the rocky reef before the lighthouse without a sign of her, he overcame his pride sufficiently to question Jim. The man looked at him with dull astonishment.

"Olooya gone," he said.

"Gone!—where?"

The Indian made a gesture to seaward which seemed to encompass the whole Pacific.

"How? With whom?" repeated his angry yet half-frightened master.

"With white man in ship. You say *you* no want Olooya—forty dollars too much. White man give fifty dollars—takee Olooya all same."

The Mermaid

ANONYMOUS

ONE Friday morn when we set sail
And our ship not far from land,
We there did espy a fair, pretty maid
With a comb and a glass in her hand,
                    her hand,
                         her hand,
With a comb and a glass in her hand.

95

And the raging seas did roar, did roar,
And the stormy winds did blow, did blow,
And we jolly sailor boys were up, up aloft,
And the landlubbers all down below,
                              below,
                                  below,
And the landsmen were all down below.

Then up spake the captain of our gallant ship,
And a gallant man was he,
"I have married a wife in fair Portsmouth town
And this night she a widow will be,
                              will be,
                                  will be,
And this night she a widow will be."

And the raging seas did roar, did roar,
And the stormy winds did blow, did blow,
And we jolly sailor boys were up, up aloft,
And the landlubbers all down below,
                              below,
                                  below,
And the landsmen were all down below.

Then next there spake the little cabin boy.
And a fair-haired lad was he,
"I've a father and a mother in fair Portsmouth town
And this night they will weep for me,
                              for me,
                                  for me,
And this night they will weep for me."

And the raging seas did roar, did roar,
And the stormy winds did blow, did blow,
And we jolly sailor boys were up, up aloft,
And the landlubbers all down below,
                              below,
                              below,
And the landsmen were all down below.

Then three times round went our gallant ship,
And three times round went she,
And for want of a life belt they both went down
As she sunk to the bottom of the sea,
                              the sea,
                              the sea,
As she sunk to the bottom of the sea.

Water Babies

CHARLES KINGSLEY

NO WATER BABIES, indeed? Why, wise men
of old said that everything on earth had
its double in the water; and you may see that that is, if not quite
true, still quite as true as most other theories which you are likely
to hear for many a day. There are land babies—then why not
water babies? Are there not water rats, water flies, water crickets,
water crabs, water tortoises, water scorpions, water tigers, and
water hogs, water cats and water dogs, sea lions, and sea bears,
sea horses and elephants, sea mice and sea urchins, sea razors

and sea pens, sea combs and sea fans; and of plants, are there not water grass, and water crowfoot, water milfoil, and so on, without end? . . .

However that may be, Tom, the young chimney sweep, was amphibious; and what is better still he was clean. For the first time in his life, he felt how comfortable it was to have nothing on him but himself. But he only enjoyed it: he did not know it, or think about it; just as you enjoy life and health and yet never think about being alive and healthy: and may it be long before you have to think about it!

He did not remember having ever been dirty. Indeed he did not remember any of his old troubles, being tired, or hungry, or beaten or sent up dark chimneys. That is not strange: for you know, when you came into this world, and became a land baby, you remembered nothing. So why should he, when he became a water baby?

Then one day Tom was sitting on a water-lily leaf, watching the gnats dance. The dragonfly had eaten as many as he wanted, and was sitting quite still and sleepy, for it was very hot and bright. The gnats (who did not care in the least for their poor brothers' death), danced a foot over his head quite happily, and a large black fly settled within an inch of his nose, and began washing his own face and combing his hair with his paws: but the dragonfly never stirred, and kept on chatting to Tom about the times when he lived under the water.

Suddenly, Tom heard the strangest noise up the stream; cooing and grunting, and whining, and squeaking, as if you had put into a bag two stock doves, nine mice, three guinea pigs, and a blind puppy, and left them there to settle themselves and make music.

He looked up the water, and there he saw a sight as strange as the noise; a great ball rolling over and over down the stream, seeming one moment of soft brown fur, and the next of shining glass: and yet it was not a ball; for sometimes it broke up and streamed away in pieces, and then it joined again; and all the while the noise came out of it louder and louder.

Tom asked the dragonfly what it could be: but, of course, with his short sight, he could not even see it, though it was not ten yards away. So he took the neatest little header into the water and started off to see for himself; and, when he came near, the ball turned out to be four or five beautiful creatures, many times larger than Tom, who were swimming about, and rolling, and diving, and twisting, and wrestling, and cuddling, and kissing, and biting, and scratching, in the most charming fashion that ever was seen. And if you don't believe me, you may go to the zoological gardens and then say, if otters at play in the water are not the merriest, lithest, gracefullest creatures you ever saw.

But, when the biggest of them saw Tom, she darted out from the rest, and cried in the water language sharply enough, "Quick children, here is something to eat indeed!" and came at poor Tom, showing such a wicked pair of eyes and such a set of sharp teeth in a grinning mouth, that Tom, who had thought her very handsome, said to himself, handsome is that handsome does, and slipped in between the water-lily roots as fast as he could, and then turned round and made faces at her.

"Come out," said the wicked old otter, "or it will be worse for you."

But Tom looked at her from between two thick roots, and shook them with all his might, making horrible faces all the while, just as he used to grin through the railings at the old women where he lived before. It was not quite well-bred, no doubt; but you know, Tom had not finished his education yet.

"Come away, children," said the otter in disgust, "it is not worth eating after all. It is only a nasty eft, which nothing eats, not even those vulgar pike in the pond."

"I am not an eft!" said Tom; "efts have tails."

"You are an eft," said the otter, very positively; "I see your two hands quite plain, and I know you have a tail."

"I tell you I have not," said Tom. "Look here!" and he turned his pretty little self quite round; and, sure enough, he had no more tail than you.

The otter might have got out of it by saying that Tom was a frog:

but like a great many other people, when she had once said a thing, she stood to it, right or wrong; so she answered:

"I say you are an eft, and therefore you are, and not fit food for gentlefolk like me and my children. You may stay there till the salmon eat you" (she knew the salmon would not, but she wanted to frighten poor Tom).

Now it befell that, on the very shore, and over the very rocks, where Tom was sitting with his friend the lobster, there walked one day the little white lady, Ellie herself, and with her a very wise man indeed—Professor Ptthmllnsprts.

So Ellie and he were walking on the rocks, and he was showing her about one in ten thousand of all the beautiful and curious things which are to be seen there. But little Ellie was not satisfied with them at all. She liked much better to play with live children, or even with dolls, which she could pretend were alive; and at last she said honestly, "I don't care about all these things, because they can't play with me, or talk to me. If there were children in the water, as there used to be, and I could see them, I should like that."

"Children in the water, you strange little duck?" said the professor.

"Yes," said Ellie. "I know there used to be children in the water, and mermaids too, and mermen. I saw them all in a picture at home, of a beautiful lady sailing in a car drawn by dolphins, and babies flying round her, and one sitting in her lap; and the mermaids swimming and playing, and the mermen trumpeting on conch shells; and it is called *The Triumph of Galatea*; and there is a burning mountain in the picture behind. It hangs on the great staircase, and I have looked at it ever since I was a baby, and dreamed about it a hundred times; and it is so beautiful, that it must be true."

So he gave her a succinct compendium of his famous paper at the British Association, in a form suited for the youthful mind. But we will not repeat it here.

Now little Ellie was, I suppose, a stupid little girl; for, instead of being convinced by Professor Ptthmllnsprts arguments, she only asked the same question over again.

"But why are there are not water babies?"

I trust and hope that it was because the professor trod at that moment on the edge of a very sharp mussel, and hurt one of his corns sadly, that he answered quite sharply, forgetting that he was a scientific man, and therefore ought to have known that he couldn't know; and that he was a logician, and therefore ought to have known that he could not prove a universal negative—I say, I trust and hope it was because the mussel hurt his corn, that the professor answered quite sharply:

"Because there ain't."

Which was not even good English.

And then he groped with his net under the weeds so violently, that, as it befell, he caught poor little Tom.

He felt the net very heavy; and lifted it out quickly, with Tom all entangled in the meshes.

"Dear me! It has actually eyes!" he cried. "Why, it must be a Cephalopod! This is most extraordinary!"

"No, I ain't," cried Tom, as loud as he could; for he did not like to be called bad names.

"It is a water baby!" cried Ellie; and of course it was.

"Water-fiddlesticks, my dear!" said the professor; and he turned away sharply.

There was no denying it. It was a water baby: and he had said a moment ago that there were none. What was he to do?

Now, if the professor had said to Ellie, "Yes, my darling, it is a water baby, and a very wonderful thing it is; and it shows how little I know of the wonders of nature, in spite of forty years' honest labor. I was just telling you that there could be no such creatures: and, behold! here is one come to confound my conceit, and show me that nature can do, and had done, beyond all that man's poor fancy can imagine. So let us thank the Maker, and Inspirer, and Lord of Nature for all His wonderful and glorious works, and try and find out something about this one":—I think that, if the professor had said that, little Ellie would have believed him more firmly, and respected him more deeply, and loved him better, than ever she had done before.

But he was of a different opinion. He hesitated a moment. He longed to keep Tom, and yet he half wished he never had caught him; and, at last, he quite longed to get rid of him. So he turned away, and poked Tom with his finger, for want of anything better to do; and said carelessly, "My dear little maid, you must have dreamed of water babies last night. Your head is so full of them."

Now Tom had been in the most horrible and unspeakable fright all the while; and had kept as quiet as he could, though he was called a Holothurian and a Cephalopod; for it was fixed in his little head that if a man with clothes on caught him, he might put clothes on him too, and make a dirty black chimney sweep of him again. But when the professor poked him, it was more than he could bear; and, between fright and rage, he turned to bay as valiantly as a mouse in a corner, and bit the professor's finger till it bled.

"Oh! ah! yah!" cried the professor, and glad of an excuse to be rid of Tom, dropped him on to the seaweed. Thence Tom dived into the water, and was gone in a moment.

And now happened a most wonderful thing. Tom came upon a water baby—a real live water baby, sitting on the white sand, very busy about a little point of rock. And when it saw Tom it looked up for a moment, and then cried, "Why, you are not one of us. You are a new baby! Oh, how delightful!"

And it ran to Tom, and Tom ran to it, and they hugged and kissed each other for ever so long, they did not know why. But they did not want any introductions there under the water.

At last Tom said, "Oh, where have you been all this while? I have been looking for you so long, and I have been so lonely."

"We have been here for days and days. There are hundreds of us about the rocks. How was it you did not see us, or hear us when we sing and romp every evening before we go home?"

Tom looked at the baby again, and then he said:

"Well this is wonderful! I have seen things just like you again and again, but I thought you were shells, or sea creatures. I never took you for water babies like myself."

"Now," said the baby, "come and help me, or I shall not have finished before my brothers and sisters come, and it is time to go home."

"What shall I help you at?"

"At this poor dear little rock; a great clumsy boulder came rolling by in the last storm, and knocked all its head off, and rubbed off all its flowers. And now I must plant it again with seaweeds, and coralline, and anemones, and I will make it the prettiest little rock garden on all the shore."

So they worked away at the rock, and planted it, and smoothed the sand down round it, and capital fun they had till the tide began to turn. And then Tom heard all the other babies coming, laughing and singing and shouting and romping; and the noise they made was just like the noise of the ripple. So he knew that he had been hearing and seeing the water babies all along; only he did not know them, because his eyes and ears were not opened.

And in they came, dozens and dozens of them, some bigger than Tom and some smaller, all in the neatest little white bathing dresses; and when they found that he was a new baby they hugged him and kissed him, and then put him in the middle and danced round him on the sand, and there was no one ever so happy as poor little Tom.

"Now then," they cried all at once, "we must come away home, we must come away home, or the tide will leave us dry. We have mended all the broken seaweed, and put all the rock pools in order, and planted all the shells again in the sand, and nobody will see where the ugly storm swept in last week."

And this is the reason why the rock pools are always so neat and clean; because the water babies come in-shore after every storm, to sweep them out, and comb them down, and put them all to rights again . . .

So Tom dived under the great white gate which never was opened yet, and went on in black darkness, at the bottom of the sea, for seven days and seven nights. And yet he was not a bit frightened. Why should he be? He was a brave English lad, whose business is to go out and see all the world.

The Wonderful Tune

T. CROFTON CROKER

AURICE CONNOR was the king, and that's no small word, of all the pipers in Munster. He could play jigs and planxties without end, and *Ollistrum's March*, and the *Eagle's Whistle*, and the *Hen's Concert*, and odd tunes of every sort and kind. But he knew one far more surprising than the rest, which had in it the power to set everything dead or alive dancing.

In what way he learned it is beyond my knowledge, for he was mighty cautious about telling how he came by so wonderful a tune. At the very first note of that tune the brogues began shaking upon the feet of all who heard it—old or young, it mattered not—just as if their brogues had the ague; then the feet began going, going, going from under them, and at last up and away with them, dancing like mad! whisking here, there, and everywhere, like a straw in a storm—there was no halting while the music lasted!

Not a fair, nor a wedding, nor a patron in the seven parishes round, was counted worth the speaking of without "blind Maurice and his pipes." His mother, poor woman, used to lead him about from one place to another just like a dog.

Down through Iveragh—a place that ought to be proud of itself, for 'tis Daniel O'Connell's country, Maurice Connor and his mother were taking their rounds. Beyond all other places Iveragh is the place for stormy coasts and steep mountains: as proper a spot it is as any in Ireland to get yourself drowned, or your neck broken on the land, should you prefer that. But, notwithstanding, in Ballinskellig bay there is a neat bit of ground, well fitted for diversion, and down from it, towards the water, is a clean smooth piece of strand, the dead image of a calm summer's sea on a moonlight night, with just the curl of the small waves upon it.

Here it was that Maurice's music had brought from all parts a great gathering of the young men and the young women—O the darlings! for 'twas not every day the strand of Trafraska was stirred up by the voice of a bigpipe. The dance began; and as pretty a rinka-fadda it was as ever was danced. "Brave music," said everybody, "and well done," when Maurice stopped.

"More power to your elbow, Maurice, and a fair wind in the bellows," cried Paddy Dorman, a humpbacked dancing-master, who was there to keep order. " 'Tis a pity," said he, "if we'd let the piper run dry after such music; 'twould be a disgrace to Iveragh, that didn't come on it since the week of the three Sundays."

"What will you drink, Maurice?" says Paddy.

"I'm no ways particular," says Maurice. "But if 'tis all the same to you, Mister Dorman, maybe you wouldn't lend me the loan of a glass of whiskey."

"I've no glass, Maurice," said Paddy. "I've only the bottle."

"Let that be no hindrance," answered Maurice, "my mouth just holds a glass to the drop; often I've tried it, sure."

So Paddy Dorman trusted him with the bottle—more fool was he; and, to his cost, he found that though Maurice's mouth might not hold more than the glass at one time, yet, owing to the hole in his throat, it took many a filling.

"That was no bad whiskey neither," says Maurice, handing back the empty bottle.

"By the holy frost, then!" says Paddy, " 'tis but cold comfort there's in that bottle now; and 'tis your word we must take for the strength of the whiskey, for you've left us no sample to judge by;" and to be sure Maurice had not.

Now I need not tell any gentleman or lady with common understanding, that if he or she was to drink an honest bottle of whiskey at one pull, it is not at all the same thing as drinking a bottle of water; and in the whole course of my life I never knew more than five men who could do so without being overtaken by the liquor. Of these Maurice Connor was not one, though he had a stiff head enough of his own—he was fairly tipsy. Don't think I blame him for it; 'tis often a good man's case; but true is the word that says, "When liquor's in, sense is out;" and puff, at a breath, before you could say "Lord, save us!" out he blasted his wonderful tune.

'Twas really then beyond all belief or telling the dancing. Maurice himself could not keep quiet, staggering now on one leg, now on the other, and rolling about like a ship in a cross sea, trying to humor the tune. There was his mother too, moving her old bones as light as the youngest girl of them all; but her dancing, no, nor the dancing of all the rest, is not worthy the speaking about to the work that was going on down upon the strand. Every inch of it covered with all manner of fish jumping and plunging about to the music, and every moment more and more would tumble in out of the water, charmed by the wonderful tune. Crabs of monstrous size spun round and round on one claw with the nimbleness of a dancing-master,

and twirled and tossed their other claws about like limbs that did
not belong to them. It was a sight surprising to behold.

But perhaps you may have heard of Florence Conry, a great Irish
poet. If you have not, he has rhymed out all about the dancing
fishes so neatly, so that it would be a thousand pities not to give you
his verses; and here's my hand at an upset of them into English:

> The big seals in motion
> Like waves of the ocean,
>   Or gouty feet prancing,
> Came heading the gay fish,
> Crabs, lobsters, and crayfish,
>   Determined on dancing.
>
> The sweet sounds they followed,
> The gasping cod swallow'd;
>   'Twas wonderful, really!
> And turbot and flounder,
> 'Mid fish that were rounder,
>   Just caper'd as gaily.
>
> John Dorys came tripping;
> Dull hake by their skipping
>   To frisk it seem'd given;
> Bright mackrel went springing,
> Like small rainbows winging
>   Their flight up to heaven.
>
> The whiting and haddock
> Left salt water paddock
>   This dance to be put in:
> Where skate with flat faces
> Edged out some odd plaices;
>   But soles kept their footing.

Sprats and herrings in powers
Of silvery showers
   All number'd outnumber'd.
And great ling so lengthy
Were there in such plenty
   The shore was encumber'd.

The scollop and oyster
Their two shells did roister,
   Like castanets fitting;
While limpets moved clearly,
And rocks very nearly
   With laughter were splitting.

Never was such an 'ullabaloo in this world, before or since; 'twas as if heaven and earth were coming together; and all out of Maurice Connor's wonderful tune!

In the height of all these doings, what should there be dancing among the outlandish set of fishes but a beautiful young woman—as beautiful as the dawn of day! She had a cocked hat upon her head: from under it her long green hair—just the colour of the sea—fell down behind, without hindrance to her dancing. Her teeth were like rows of pearl; her lips for all the world looked like red coral; and she had an elegant gown, as white as the foam of the wave, with little rows of purple and red seaweeds settled out upon it; for you never yet saw a lady, or a mermaid, who had not a good notion of dressing herself.

Up she danced at last to Maurice, who was flinging his feet from under him as fast as hops—for nothing in this world could keep still while that tune of his was going on—and says she to him, chanting it out with a voice as sweet as honey—

   "I'm a lady of honour
     Who lives in the sea:
   Come down, Maurice Connor,

And be married to me.
  Silver plates and gold dishes
    You shall have, and shall be
  The King of the fishes,
    When you're married to me."

Drink was strong in Maurice's head, and out he chanted in return for her great civility. It is not every lady, may be, that would be after making such an offer to a blind piper; therefore 'twas only right in him to give her as good as she gave herself—so says Maurice:

  "I'm obliged to you, madam;
    Off a gold dish or plate,
  If a king, and I had 'em,
    I could dine in great state.
  With your own father's daughter
    I'd be sure to agree;
  But to drink the salt water
    Wouldn't do so with me!"

The lady looked at him quite amazed, and swinging her head from side to side like a great scholar, "Well," says she, "Maurice, if you're not a poet, where is poetry to be found?"

In this way they kept on at it, framing high compliments; one answering the other, and their feet going with the music as fast as their tongues. All the fish kept dancing too: Maurice heard the clatter and was afraid to stop playing lest it might be displeasing to the fish, and not knowing what so many of them may take it into their heads to do to him if they got vexed.

Well, the lady with the green hair kept on coaxing of Maurice with soft speeches, till at last she overpersuaded him to promise to marry her, and be king over the fishes, great and small. Maurice was well fitted to be their king, if they wanted one that could make them dance; and he surely would drink, barring the salt water, with any fish of them all.

When Maurice's mother saw him, with that unnatural thing in the form of a green-haired lady as his guide, and he and she dancing down together so lovingly to the water's edge, through the thick of the fishes, she called out after him to stop and come back. "Oh then," says she, "as if I was not widow enough before, there he is going away from me to be married to that scaly woman. And who knows but 'tis grandmother I may be to a hake or a cod—Lord help and pity me, but 'tis a mighty unnatural thing! and may be 'tis boiling and eating my own grandchild I'll be, with a bit of salt butter, and I not knowing it! Oh Maurice, Maurice, if there's any love or nature left in you, come back to your own old mother, who reared you like a decent Christian!" Then the poor woman began to cry and ullagone so finely that it would do any one good to hear her.

Maurice was not long getting to the rim of the water; there he kept playing and dancing on as if nothing was the matter, and a great thundering wave coming in towards him ready to swallow him up alive; but as he could not see it, he did not fear it. His mother it was who saw it plainly through the big tears that were rolling down her cheeks; and though she saw it, and her heart was aching as much as ever a mother's heart ached for a son, she kept dancing, dancing all the time for the bare life of her. Certain it was she could not help it, for Maurice never stopped playing that wonderful tune of his.

He only turned the bothered ear to the sound of his mother's voice, fearing it might put him out in his steps, and all the answer he made back was, "Whisht with you, mother—sure I'm going to be king over the fishes down in the sea, and for a token of luck, and a sign that I'm alive and well, I'll send you every twelvemonth on this day, a piece of burned wood to Trafraska." Maurice had not the power to say a word more, for the strange lady with the green hair, seeing the wave just upon them covered him up with herself in a thing like a cloak with a big hood to it, and the wave curling over twice as high as their heads, burst upon the strand, with a rush and a roar that might be heard as far as Cape Clear.

That day twelvemonth the piece of burned wood came ashore in Trafraska. It was a queer thing for Maurice to think of sending all

111

the way from the bottom of the sea. A gown or a pair of shoes would have been something like a present for his poor mother; but he had said it, and he kept his word. The bit of burned wood regularly came ashore on the appointed day for as good, ay, and better than a hundred years. The day is now forgotten, and maybe that is the reason why people say how Maurice Connor has stopped sending the luck-token to his mother. Poor woman, she did not live to get as much as one of them; for what through the loss of Maurice, and the fear of eating her own grandchildren, she died in three weeks after the dance. Some say it was the fatigue that killed her, but whichever it was, Mrs. Connor was decently buried with her own people.

Seafaring people have often heard, off the coast of Kerry, on a still night, the sound of music coming up from the water; and some, who have had good ears, could plainly distinguish Maurice Connor's voice singing these words to his pipes:

"Beautiful shore, with thy spreading strand,
Thy crystal water, and diamond sand;
Never would I have parted from thee,
But for the sake of my fair ladie."

Siren Song

JOAN AIKEN

Oʜ what are they a-doing of, the Sirens on the rocks?
  A-nodding and a-gossiping and knitting winter socks,
  In saucy stripes and gaudy checks and polka dots and plaids,
  When not engaged in singing songs to simple sailor lads.
Yo-ho, me lads, and so, me lads, you may bet your monthly money,
  It's purl and plain upon the main that keeps the Sirens sunny.

Oʜ what are they a-doing of, the Mermaids in the grottoes?
  A-giving cracker parties, and reading out the mottoes?
  But no, they crochet winter vests to keep away the cold
  And play upon their lutes and flutes and triangles of gold.
Yo-ho, me lads, and so, me lads, attend this wisdom weighty
  Its crochet on the ocean blue that keeps the mermaids matey.

Aɴᴅ what about the Loreleis a-sitting by the streams
  Enticing with their lullabies young oarsmen into dreams?
  When not engaged in lullabies they weave warm underwear
  To keep them from the clammy rocks and chilly winter air.
Yo-ho, me lads, and so, me lads, you take, if you are wise,
  Some shuttles and some wool to please the looming Loreleis.

The Blue Men
of the Minch

ELIZABETH SHEPPARD JONES

THE BLUE MEN lived under the sea near the Shiant Isles, and were much feared by the sailors who had to sail their boats through the strait of the Minch. When the Blue Men were awake, they disturbed the waters even on the most peaceful days and dragged down ships to their doom at the bottom of the sea. Their strait was calm only when they were asleep in their underwater caves or when they floated happily on the top of the water. And if they were seen playing and laughing off the headland of Rudha Hunish, then the people of North-western Skye were warned that a wild storm was on its way. The fishermen believed that the Blue Men often followed their boats, and, when the weather grew suddenly rough, they might seize hold of the helm or keel and try to swamp them. The Blue Men particularly disliked to see any large vessel dare to sail in their waters, and some captains were so afraid of these fierce men of the deep sea they would sail northwards round the Shiant Isles rather than take the short cut through the strait.

Some of the Blue Men were always posted at certain spots in the water, and, as soon as they sighted a vessel, they would dive off to tell their Chief, who immediately called together the rest of his followers. Then a great horde of these unfriendly mermen attacked the ship in question. But, first, the Chief shouted a challenge in two lines of Gaelic verse, and only if the skipper could not reply with two lines of verse was the ship seized and wrecked.

One day, when the wind was screaming across the sea and whipping the waves into a fury, a great ship, its white sails blowing bravely, appeared at the southern end of the strait. The Blue Men on guard gave the usual warning to their Chief, and soon an army of them arose to the surface of the sea and gazed in wonder at the handsome ship as it swiftly ploughed its way towards them. Some of them grasped the keel but it was too heavy for them to move, others banged the side of the vessel but the smooth planks were too thick for them to pierce.

The Chief pulled himself waist high out of the waves and shouted to the captain.

"What do you want, Chief of the Blue Men?" shouted the brave skipper.

The Chief called out his first two lines of verse:

"Man of the black cap, what do you say
As your proud ship cleaves the brine?"

The Captain promptly replied with his two lines:

"My speedy ship takes the shortest way
And I'll follow you line by line."

115

The Chief of the Blue Men sang out:

> "My men are eager, my men are ready
> To drag you below the waves."

The Captain sang back:

> "My ship is speedy, my ship is steady;
> If it sank it would wreck your caves."

The Chief had never before been answered so well and so quickly. He knew himself to be outwitted and he and his men sank quickly below the waves, while the ship went peacefully on its way through the Minch.

Melusine

HELEN O'CLERY

Deep in the heart of the Coulombier forest in the
west of France, Melusine sat on the edge of a
crystal-clear pool.

She was thinking dreamily about the dim and far-off past
when her own immortal father had done a grievous wrong to her
immortal mother, and Melusine, to punish him, had imprisoned
her father under a mountain. From time to time he showed his
old restless spirit by causing a volcanic eruption.

Naturally some of the other immortals disapproved of Melusine's high-handed tactics. After all, they said to themselves, if this sort of retaliation becomes popular among our maidens, there is no knowing where some of us might find ourselves. So, to provide an example to other immortal daughters, they punished Melusine by turning her into a serpent from the waist down.

Melusine accepted her punishment without resentment. However, she was tired of the immortals and their everlasting strife. She wanted to marry a true mortal man with a heart and a soul, and no powers of enchantment. In time, and by certain promises, she persuaded the gods to let her be herself again.

Thus, on a fateful day, she splashed the clear spring water with her naked feet and smiled triumphantly because they had once again replaced the serpent's tail. They were small, white and very pretty. Very pretty indeed. She lifted them out of the water, and the dappled sunlight, as it gleamed through the leafy trees, twinkled upon them.

From far away in some distant corner of the forest she heard a hunter's horn and the baying of the hounds. This did not surprise her for she knew all that went on in this part of the world. It was her domain, so to speak, though she did not own it; she merely watched over it.

Melusine, unlike some immortals, did not often meddle with the affairs of men. She felt that they were quite well able to look after their own business and if they did not quarrel so violently as the immortals, nor wreak vengeance upon each other so dramatically, this was merely because they were human.

The sound of the horn and the baying of the hounds grew fainter. Melusine stirred the water thoughtfully with her newly-released toes and thought about the human hunters in the woods. The Count de Poitiers was well up in the lead behind the hounds, his black steed flecked with foam as he charged through thickets, jumped fallen tree trunks and splashed through streams in hot pursuit of the excited hounds and the still far distant stag.

De Poitiers was lord of all this province, a great leader of men and a very wealthy person. But Melusine had no need of either power or wealth, and a great lord must watch over his people, whether in his own household or in the outlying countryside. She wanted a trusting heart, not a watchful eye.

Almost on the heels of de Poitiers came his cousin, the Count Forez, a wealthy fellow too, and powerful in his way, but of a jealous disposition. This Melusine liked even less, so she let her mind skip to his younger brother Raymond, neither Lord nor Count, but a handsome, fearless, penniless knight. She smiled and again stirred the water with her toe. As she did so Raymond's horse stumbled. He did not fall, but limped a little as he regained his stride. Raymond dismounted, examined the horse's legs for injury but finding none, mounted once again.

By this time the hunt had swept on out of sight. Dusk was falling and the young knight, thinking his horse was probably tired, decided to return alone to his cousin's castle. As he did not know his way through the forest, he left the reins loose on the horse's neck, trusting the beast to find his own way home. But the horse was thirsty and went instead toward the pool beside which Melusine sat.

She was bending over the water, combing her long black hair and gazing at her own reflection as if unaware of the approaching knight, when Raymond came up behind her. He dismounted and let his horse go free as he gazed in fascination at the reflection of the most beautiful face he had ever seen in all his life. But when Melusine turned her head slowly and smiled at him, he was so enthralled that he knew he could never love any other woman. His heart beat furiously and as he struggled to find words, the beautiful maiden spoke to him.

"Raymond," she said, "I am Melusine, and I have been waiting for you." Her voice was as beautiful as her hair, her eyes, her face and her whole exquisite form. He did not pause to wonder how she knew his name, why she was waiting for him, how she knew he would come, or even who she was. It was enough that she had spoken and that she was evidently pleased to see him.

"I am a poor knight," he said to her sadly, "but if I had land and riches I would lay them at your feet."

"Land and riches shall be yours," Melusine replied. "Go to your cousin, the Count de Poitiers, at the end of the day's hunt and ask if he will give you this spring and as much land as can be encompassed by the skin of a deer killed in today's hunt. Ask for no more, and no less."

Raymond did not seem surprised by these words; he was too madly in love to be surprised by anything. So he rode away as soon as his horse had refreshed himself from the pool, and this time his steed made straight for home.

There was great stir and excitement at the castle. The day's hunting had been good and a feast was now in preparation. The Count de Poitiers welcomed Raymond with open arms, for he had missed his young cousin and feared he might have lost his way in the woods.

"You must join the revels with us tonight, even though you were not in at the kill," he said, putting his arm around Raymond's shoulders and leading him toward the house.

"Not tonight, if you will excuse me," Raymond said. "I have met a maiden whom I wish to marry, but I can only do so if you will grant me the spring which lies deep in the heart of the forest, and as much land as can be encompassed by the hide of a deer killed in today's chase."

"My dear fellow," said the Count, laughing as he slapped his cousin on the back. "Love has gone to your head! What girl would marry you on such a small fortune? But never mind, I will give you broad acres, a handsome castle and enough money to set up house as a knight should."

"No, dear cousin," Raymond said, "although I thank you heartily for the kind thought, I want no more and no less than I have asked for."

"They shall be yours," the Count replied, "for indeed, this maiden must love you as madly as you love her if she is content with so little."

The Count then ordered his servants to skin the largest deer killed that day, and he presented the hide to Raymond. He was still obviously amused by the request and as his cousin was about to depart he called after him, "I would meet this beauteous maiden who is so modest in her demands."

"You shall, you shall," Raymond replied. "You will be the guest of honour at our wedding." Then he flung the deerskin over his shoulder, remounted his horse and rode off into the moonlight.

When he reached the spring in the heart of the forest, Melusine was still there, but a dozen beautiful girls garlanded with spring flowers were now dancing around her in great joy. They bowed down as Raymond approached and their mistress stood up to go to meet him.

"Well done," she said as Raymond spread the deerskin on the ground at her feet, smiling ruefully at the small area of ground which it encompassed.

Melusine clapped her hands and from the shadows cast by the moonlit trees dozens of little men with scissors in their hands ran forward. They surrounded the deerskin and sat cross-legged in a circle. Then immediately they began to cut it into very narrow strips. These strips they cut finer and still finer till they were like gossamer thread, which they lifted on their shoulders and carried through the woods and over the fertile plain till they had encompassed a vast estate and the beginning of the deerskin thread was joined to the end.

"There is your estate," Melusine said to Raymond, throwing her arms out right and left to indicate the extent of it. "Now all we need is a castle, and that's easy."

"How easy?" he asked, gazing into the beautiful face of his beloved, so that he hardly knew what he said.

"So easy," Melusine replied, clapping her hands once again. When another relay of helpers answered she handed them a heap of white quartz stones and a little crystal-clear water from the pool. "Make a clearing in the forest over there," she said, pointing. "This must be my private garden. . . . There you must erect the palace, surrounded by a domain we will call Lusignan, which will become famous in French history in years to come."

Her attendants set to work. Before dawn a walled garden of the most exquisite beauty had been laid out around the spring water pool. And before dawn also, a palace of glistening quartz had been built deep in the heart of the forest.

"Now," said Raymond, who was still too dazed by Melusine's beauty and his love for her to wonder how he had acquired such a rich and wonderful estate so easily, "now may I ask you to marry me?" He went down on one knee and gazed up at his ladylove imploringly, as knights were wont to do in the days of chivalry.

"I will," said Melusine, lowering her beautiful eyes in a becoming display of maidenly modesty, "if you will promise never to see me on Saturdays, and never to ask me what I do on that day of the week."

"I swear it, on my word as an honourable knight of France," said Raymond, "and may I lose you for ever if I break my word."

Melusine gazed at Raymond and saw that she had chosen well. He was as trusting, chivalrous and pure-hearted as he was handsome. She smiled happily and put her hand in his. Then, arm in arm, they walked through their new palace, scarcely noticing the magnificence of the rooms and the fine furnishings, so intent were they with one another and with making plans for their wedding.

All the necessary preparations would have been no trouble to Melusine if she had chosen to use her magic powers. But she had decided to behave like a real human being, and found herself as happy as the days were long. Even her servants had to forget their fairy origin and sweep floors, clean windows and set tables, like any other servants.

As Raymond had promised, he invited the Count de Poitiers to his wedding and also, besides a great many other people his brother, Count Forez. All were astonished by the magnificence of Raymond's court, for they had thought him to be a penniless though chivalrous knight. De Poitiers was full of admiration and delighted by his cousin's good fortune, especially when he met the charming and beautiful bride. But Forez was envious because he feared that before long he himself would be overshadowed by his own younger brother in popularity and power.

When the wedding guests had departed, Raymond and Melusine settled down to a happy married life. Except for Saturdays, when Melusine was never seen either by her husband or any other human being, she rarely left Raymond's side. Together they rode through the estate to see how the crops were doing and to give instructions here or there. Melusine got to know the people living in the cottages, and never tired of admiring their neat gardens, their spotless kitchens and their rosy-cheeked children, so that she was beloved by them all.

In due course, Melusine and Raymond had a son. He was a beautiful boy, with dark eyes of unusual brilliance. As he grew up it became apparent that besides many excellent qualities he had better eyesight than any other human being. Their second son had ears of a curious shape. He also was handsome, brave and clever, besides having more acute hearing than any other human being. Their third son was marked with a lion's paw and had all the good qualities of his brothers, though he excelled even them in courage.

Raymond and Melusine had ten sons in all. Each had a special gift and a slight peculiarity, but all were handsome, brave, clever and beloved by everyone. They grew up to do great deeds and to win distinction and riches. As each in turn grew to manhood, Melusine had a palace built for him and invited the most beautiful and high-born maidens of the land to come to a great ball, so that he might choose one for a bride.

And so the years went on very happily indeed, until one fateful Saturday when Raymond's envious brother, Count Forez, came to visit him. Now, on this particular Saturday, as on every other Saturday, Melusine was not at home. Forez cross-questioned his brother about this, and Raymond explained quite frankly that he never saw his wife on Saturdays.

"Why?" asked Forez eagerly.

"I don't know why," Raymond retorted. "It is Melusine's wish and that is enough for me."

"Simpleton!" His brother laughed knowingly. "Have you never even wondered what Melusine does on Saturdays?" He saw an opportunity to make mischief between the brother whom he envied and Melusine who was, even now when she had ten grown-up sons, more beautiful than his own wife had ever been.

"That is her affair," Raymond said with a shrug.

"Perhaps, perhaps," Forez replied in a doubtful tone. "But if she were my wife, I would certainly want to know. Have you never looked at your sons and wondered why each one has some quality which you have not?"

"Sons are rarely the exact replicas of their fathers," Raymond reminded his brother without being unkind enough to add that Forez's own sons deserved no special praise.

Nevertheless, Raymond sometimes wondered what Melusine did on Saturdays, and took to wandering about in an aimless sort of way when she was absent.

One Saturday as he was passing the walled garden which surrounded the spring where he had first met Melusine, Raymond heard splashing and singing. The voice sounded like that of Melusine, and without meaning to pry on her, he went to the wrought-iron gates of the garden, intending to go in. Finding them firmly locked, he stood on tiptoe and stared into the garden. Between the beautiful magnolia trees he could just catch a glimpse of the crystal-clear spring, and swimming about in it he saw his wife.

She dived down out of sight, then she came up again, head and shoulders above the water. Flinging her long, wet hair back off her face, she sang a melancholy song, almost a dirge.

Raymond shivered. He knew now that on Saturdays his wife spent her time swimming about in the spring water all by herself, and this discovery made him feel quite ashamed of the vague suspicions which his brother had put into his head.

Still leaning on the gate, Raymond continued to gaze at his beloved wife who had not yet seen him. And the longer he stood there, the more melancholy he became. Raymond himself could not account for his sadness, but he could not shake off the feeling of impending disaster. As he watched Melusine she never once came up out of the water, so he could not possibly guess that although the immortals had permitted her to resume her own beautiful shape and form for six days of the week, she was still doomed to her serpent's tail on Saturdays until she had bathed for many hours in the clear, purifying spring pool. . . . Nor did he know that if, during this ceremony, she were seen by mortal eyes, she would never more be able to return to human form.

Once more Melusine came to the surface, flung her hair back off her face and began to sing. But on that instant she chanced to glance towards the garden gate. She stared at Raymond for one long terrible instant, during which her eyes grew wider and wider as they filled with tears of utter dismay. Slowly she rose up out of the water, higher, higher, and higher. Raymond had never ceased to admire her beauty, and now, if possible, she seemed more beautiful than ever—down as far as the waistline, but from there on she was now a sinuous serpent.

Raymond gasped with horror as more and more of that writhing tail rose out of the water. Then, with a wild shriek of anguish, Melusine flew up into the sky where a great black bank of cloud engulfed her.

Though Melusine was never again seen by her sorrowing husband or by any other mortal eyes, she still watched over the region which had been hers, and where, for what now seemed but a short while, she had been supremely happy. When Raymond died of sorrow, her wild cry echoed and reechoed through the castle, and for ever afterwards, all down through the ages when danger threatened the house of Lusignan, or one of her descendants lay dying, her wailing could be heard all through the forest of Coulombier.

"Pousser des cris de Melusine" is to this day a vividly descriptive phrase in the French language.

The Mermaid
of Margate

THOMAS HOOD

On Margate beach, where the sick one roams,
  And the sentimental reads;
Where the maiden flirts, and the widow comes
  Like the ocean—to cast her weeds;—

Where urchins wander to pick up shells,
  And the Cit to spy at the ships,—
Like the water gala at Sadler's Wells,—
  And the Chandler for watery dips;—

There's a maiden sits by the ocean brim,
  As lovely and fair as sin;
But woe, deep water and woe to him,
  That she snareth like Peter Fin!

126

Her head is crowned with pretty sea wares,
    And her locks are golden and loose,
And seek to her feet, like other folks' heirs,
    To stand, of course, in her shoes.

And all day long she combeth them well,
    With a sea shark's prickly jaw;
And her mouth is just like a rose-lipped shell,
    The fairest that man e'er saw.

And the fishmonger, humble as love may be,
    Hath planted his seat by her side;
"Good even, fair maid! Is thy lover at sea,
    To make thee so watch the tide?"

She turned about with her pearly brows,
    And clasped him by the hand;
"Come, love, with me; I've a bonny house
    On the golden Goodwin sand."

And then she gave him a siren kiss,
    No honeycomb e'er was sweeter;
Poor wretch! how little he dremt for this
    That Peter should be salt-Peter:

And away with her prize to the wave she leapt,
    Not walking, as damsels do,
With toe and heel, as she ought to have stept,
    But she hopt like a kangaroo;

One plunge, and then the victim was blind,
    Whilst they galloped across the tide;
At last, on the bank he waked in his mind,
    And the Beauty was by his side.

One half on the sand, and half in the sea,
　　But his hair began to stiffen;
For when he looked where her feet should be,
　　She had no more feet than Miss Biffen!

But a scaly tail, of a dolphin's growth,
　　In the dabbling brine did soak:
At last she opened her pearly mouth,
　　Like an oyster, and thus she spoke:

"You crimpt my father, who was a skate,—
　　And my sister you sold—a maid:
So here remain for a fish'ry fate,
　　For lost you are, and betrayed!"

And away she went, with a sea gull's scream
　　And a splash of her saucy tail;
In a moment he lost the silvery gleam
　　That shone on her splendid mail.

The sun went down with a blood-red flame,
　　And the sky grew cloudy and black,
And the tumbling billows like leap-frog came,
　　Each over the other's back.

Ah me! it had been a beautiful scene,
　　With the safe *terra-firma* round;
But the green water hillocks all seemed to him
　　Like those in a churchyard ground;

And Christians love in the turf to lie,
　　Not in watery graves to be;
Nay, the very fishes will sooner die
　　On the land than in the sea.

And whilst he stood, the watery strife
 Encroached on every hand,
And the ground decreased,—his moments of life
 Seemed measured, like Time's, by sand.

And still the waters foamed in, like ale,
 In front, and on either flank,
He knew that Goodwin and Co. must fail,
 There was such a run on the bank.

A little more, and a little more,
 The surges came tumbling in,
He sang the evening hymn twice o'er,
 And thought of every sin.

Each flounder and plaice lay cold at his heart,
 As cold as his marble slab;
And he thought he felt, in every part,
 The pincers of scalded crab.

The squealing lobsters that he had boiled,
 And the little potted shrimps,
All the horny prawns he had ever spoiled,
 Gnawed into his soul, like imps!

And the billows were wandering to and fro,
 And the glorious sun was sunk,
And Day, getting black in the face, as though
 Of the nightshade she had drunk.

Had there been but a smuggler's cargo adrift,
 One tub, or keg, to be seen,
It might have given his spirits a lift
 Or an anker where Hope might lean.

But there was not a box or a beam afloat,
    To raft him from that sad place;
Not a skiff, not a yawl, or a mackerel boat
    Nor a smack upon Neptune's face.

At last, his lingering hope to buoy,
    He saw a sail and a mast,
And called "Ahoy!"—but it was not a hoy,
    And so the vessel went past.

And with saucy wing that flapped in his face,
    The wild bird about him flew,
With a shrilly scream, that twitted his case,
    "Why, thou art a sea gull too!"

And lo! the tide was over his feet;
    O! his heart began to freeze,
And slowly to pulse:—in another beat
    The wave was up to his knees.

He was deafened amidst the mountain tops,
    And the salt spray blinded his eyes,
And washed away the other salt drops
    That grief had caused to arise:—

But just as his body was all afloat,
    And the surges above him broke,
He was saved from the hungry deep by a boat
    Of Deal—(but builded of oak).

The skipper gave him a dram, as he lay,
    And chafed his shivering skin;
And the Angel returned that was flying away
    With the spirit of Peter Fin!

Translated by R. Nisbet Bain

The Little Mermaid

HANS CHRISTIAN ANDERSEN

FAR OUT in the sea the water is as blue as the leaves of the loveliest cornflower and as clear as the purest glass, but it is very deep, deeper than ever anchor yet reached; many church towers would have to be piled one on top of the other to reach right up from the bottom to the surface of the water. Down there dwell the Seafolk. Now you must by no means fancy that there is nothing there but a bare white sand-bank; no, the most wondrous trees and plants grow there, the stalks and leaves of which are so supple that they move to and

131

fro at the least motion of the water, just as if they were living beings. All the fish, small and great, dart about among the branches just as the birds do in the air up here. In the deepest spot of all lies the Sea King's palace. The walls are of coral and the long, pointed windows of the clearest sort of amber, but the roof is of mussel shells which open and shut as the water flows; it looks lovely, for in every one of the shells lies a glistening pearl. Any one of these pearls would be the glory of a queen's crown.

The Sea King down there had been a widower for many years, but his old mother kept house for him; she was a wise woman, but proud of her noble birth, and that was why she always went about with twelve oysters on her tail, the other notabilities being allowed to carry only six. Nevertheless she was very popular, especially because she doted upon the little Sea Princesses, her granddaughters. They were six pretty children, but the youngest was the loveliest of them all; her skin was as delicately tinted as a rose leaf, her eyes as blue as the deepest lake, but, like all the others, she had no feet, her body ended in a fish's tail. The livelong day they used to play in the palace down there in the great saloon where living flowers grew out of the walls. The large amber windows were opened and so the fishes swam into them just as the swallows fly in to us when we open our windows, but the fishes swam right up to the little princesses, ate out of their hands and let themselves be petted.

Outside the palace was a large garden full of bloodred and dark blue trees; the fruits there shone like gold, and the flowers like burning fire, and the stalks and leaves were always moving to and fro. The soil itself was of the finest sand, but as blue as sulphur flames. A wondrous blue gleam lay over everything down there; one would be more inclined to fancy that one stood high up in the air and saw nothing but sky above and beneath than that one was at the bottom of the sea. During a calm, too, one could catch a glimpse of the sun; it looked like a purple flower from the cup of which all light streamed forth.

Every one of the little princesses had her own little garden plot where she could dig and plant as she liked; one gave her flower pot

132

the form of a whale, another preferred hers to look like a little mermaid, but the youngest made hers quite round like the sun and would only have flowers which shone red like it. She was a strange child, silent and pensive, and when the other sisters adorned their gardens with the strangest things they got from stranded vessels, all that she would have, besides the rosy-red flowers which resembled the sun up above, was a pretty marble statue of a lovely boy, hewn out of bright white stone, which had sunk to the bottom of the sea during a shipwreck. She planted by this statue a rosy-red weeping willow; it grew splendidly and hung over the statue with its fresh branches, right down toward the blue sandy bottom where the shadows took a violet hue and moved to and fro like the branches; it looked as if roots and treetop were playing at kissing each other.

Her greatest joy was to hear about the world of mankind up above. She made her old grandmother tell her all she knew about ships and towns, men and beasts; and what especially struck her as wonderfully nice was that the flowers which grew upon the earth should give forth fragrance, which they did not do at the bottom of the sea; and that the woods were green and the fish among the branches could sing so loudly and beautifully that it was a joy to listen to them; it was the little birds that her grandmother called fishes. The little mermaid would not otherwise have understood her, for she had never seen a bird.

"When you have reached your fifteenth year," said her grandmother, "you may duck up out of the sea and sit in the moonshine on the rocks to see the big ships which sail by; woods and cities you shall see."

In the following year one of the sisters would be fifteen years old, but how about the others? Each one was a year younger than the one before, and so the youngest would have to wait five whole years before she could come up from the bottom of the sea and see how things are with us. But each one promised to tell the others what she saw and what she thought loveliest on the first day; for their grandmother did not tell them half enough, there was so much they wanted to know about.

None of the mermaids was so full of longing as the youngest, the very one who had the longest time to wait and was so silent and pensive. Many a time she stood by the open window and looked up through the dark blue water where the fishes steered about with their fins and tails. She could see the moon and stars; of course, they shone quite faintly, but at the same time they looked twice as large through the water as they look to us, and when something like a dark cloud glided across them, she knew that it was either a whale swimming over them, or else a ship with many people on board; they certainly never dreamed that a pretty little mermaid stood down below and stretched her white arms up towards the keel.

And now the eldest princess was fifteen years old and might ascend to the surface of the water. When she came back she had hundreds of things to tell about, but the nicest of all, she said, was to lie in the moonshine on a sandbank in the calm sea, and see, close by the shore, the large town where the lights were twinkling, like hundreds of stars, and hear the music and the noise and bustle of carts and men, and look at the many church towers and spires, and hear the bells ringing. It was just because she could not go ashore that she longed so for all these things.

Oh! how the youngest sister listened, and ever afterwards, when she stood in the evening close by the open window, and looked up through the dark blue water, she thought of the great city with all its noise and bustle, and then she thought she heard the church bells ringing down where she was.

The next year the second sister got leave to mount up through the water and swim where she liked. She ducked up just as the sun was going down and she thought that the prettiest sight of all. The whole sky had looked like gold, she said, and the clouds—well, their beauty she absolutely could not describe. All red and violet they had sailed right over her; but far quicker than they, a flock of wild swans had flown right over the place where the sun stood, like a long white veil. The second mermaid also swam toward the sun, but it sank; and the rosy gleam it left behind it was swallowed up by the sea and the clouds.

A year after that, the third sister came up to the surface; she was the boldest of them all, so she swam up a broad river which ran into the sea. She saw pretty green hillocks with vines around them, castles and country houses peeped forth from among the woods; she heard all the birds singing and the sun shone so hotly that she frequently had to duck down under the water to cool her burning face. In a little creek she came upon a whole swarm of human children; they were running about quite naked and splashing in the water. She wanted to play with them but they ran away in terror, and a little black beast came up. It was a dog, but she had never seen a dog before; it barked so savagely at her that she was frightened and sought the open sea again, but never could she forget the splendid woods, the green heights and the pretty children who could swim in the water although they had no fishes' tails.

The fourth sister was not so bold; she remained out in the middle of the sea and said that that was the nicest of all; you could see for miles and miles round about, and the sky above stood there just like a large glass bell. Ships she had seen too, but far away they looked like sea mews; the merry dolphins had turned somersaults and the big whales had spouted water up out of their nostrils, so that it looked like hundreds of fountains playing all around.

And now it was the turn of the fifth sister. Her birthday happened to be in the winter time, and therefore she saw what the others had not seen the first time. The sea turned green and huge icebergs swam about. Each one looked like a pearl, she said, and yet was far larger than the church towers which men build. They showed themselves in the strangest shapes and gleamed like diamonds. She had sat upon one of the largest, and all vessels had cruised far out in terror while she sat there and let the wind flutter her long streaming hair. Toward evening the sky was overcast with clouds; it thundered and lightened while the black sea lifted the large ice blocks high up and let them shine in the strong glare of the lightning. The ships took in their sails; distress and horror reigned, but the mermaid sat calmly on her swimming iceberg and saw the blue thunderbolts strike down in zigzags into the shining sea.

The first time any of the sisters rose to the surface of the water she was always enraptured at the new and beautiful things she saw, but when they now, as grown-up girls, had leave to go up whenever they chose, they became quite indifferent about it; they longed for home, and in about a month's time or so would say that it was nicest of all down below, for there one felt so thoroughly at ease.

Very often in the evenings, the five sisters would take each other's arms and mount up in a group to the surface of the water; they had nice voices, sweeter than any human voice, and when it was blowing a gale and they had good reason to believe that a ship might be lost, they would swim before that ship and sing so sweetly of how pleasant it was at the bottom of the sea, and bid the sailors not to be afraid to come down. But the sailors could not understand their words. They fancied it was the storm, nor did they ever get to see any of the beautiful things down below, for when the ship sank, the crew were drowned and only came as dead men to the Sea King's palace.

When her sisters thus ascended, arm in arm, high up through the sea, the little sister would remain behind all alone and look up after them, and she felt as if she must cry; but the mermaid has no tears and so she suffers all the more.

"Oh, if only I were fifteen years old!" said she. "I know that I shall quite get to love the world up above there and the men who live and dwell there."

And at last she was fifteen years old.

"Well, now at last we have you off our hands," said her grandmother, the old Queen Dowager. "Come here and let me make you look nice like your sisters," and she placed a wreath of white lilies on her hair, but every petal in every flower was the half of a pearl, and the old lady made eight large oysters cling fast to the Princess's tail to show her high rank.

"But it hurts me so!" said the little mermaid.

"Yes, one must suffer a little for the sake of appearances," said the old lady.

Oh, how much she would have liked to tear off all this finery and lay aside her heavy wreath! The little red flowers from her garden suited her much better but she dared not do it. "Farewell!" she said and mounted, light and bright as a bubble, up through the water.

The sun had just gone down as she lifted her head above the sea, but all the clouds were still shining like roses and gold, and in the midst of the pale pink sky sparkled the evening star, clear and lovely. The air was mild and fresh and the sea as still as a mirror. A black ship with three masts lay upon it. Only a single sail was up, for not a breath of wind was stirring and the sailors sprawled about on the masts and rigging. The little mermaid heard music and singing and as the evening grew darker, hundreds of variegated lamps were lit; it looked as if the flags of all nations were waving in the air. The little mermaid swam right up to the cabin window and every time the water raised her in the air she could look in through the mirror-bright panes where so many stylishly-dressed people were standing.

The handsomest of them all was certainly the young Prince with the large black eyes (he could not have been more than sixteen years old); it was his birthday and that was the reason for the festivity. The sailors were dancing upon the deck, and when the young Prince stepped out, more than a hundred rockets rose into the air; they shone as bright as day, so that the little mermaid was quite frightened and ducked down beneath the water, but she soon stuck up her head again, and then it was as if all the stars of heaven were falling down on her. Never had she seen such fireworks. Large suns whizzed round and round, splendid fiery fish swung about in the blue air, and everything was reflected in the clear, calm sea. On the ship itself, it was so light that you could see every little rope and spar, to say nothing of the men. But ah! how lovely the young Prince was, and how he pressed people's hands and laughed and smiled while the music sounded through the lovely night.

It grew late but the little mermaid could not tear her eyes away from the ship and the handsome Prince. The variegated lights were put out. No more rockets rose into the air, no more salvos were fired, but deep down in the sea there was a murmuring and a roaring.

She meanwhile sat upon the water and rocked up and down with it so that she could look into the cabin.

But the ship now took a swifter course, one sail spread out after the other, the roll of the billows grew stronger, it lightninged far away. Oh! there would be a frightful storm; that is why the sailors were now reefing the sails. The huge ship rocked to and fro as it flew along the wild ocean: the water rose like big black mountains, rolling right over the masts, but the ship ducked like a swan down among the lofty billows and let herself be lifted up again on the towering water. The little mermaid thought it rich sport, but not so the sailors; the ship strained and cracked, the thick planks bent at the violent shock of the sea, the mast snapped right in the middle like a reed, and the ship heeled over on her side while the water rushed into the cabin.

And now the little mermaid saw that they were in danger; she herself had to beware of the spars and wreckage of the ship which drove along upon the water. For a moment it was so pitch dark that she could see nothing at all, but when it lightninged it was bright enough for her to see everything on the ship. Everybody there was tumbling about. She looked for the young Prince especially and, when the ship went to pieces, she saw him sink down into the deep sea. She immediately became quite delighted, for now he would come down to her, but then it occurred to her that men cannot live in the water and that it was only as a corpse that he could reach her father's palace. Die he must not, oh no; and so she swam among the drifting spars and planks, quite forgetting that they might crush her. She ducked down beneath the water and rose aloft again on the billows, until, at last, she came to the young Prince, who could scarcely swim another stroke in the raging sea. His arms and legs began to fail him, his beautiful eyes closed. He would have died if the little mermaid had not come. She held his head above the water and let the billows drive him and her however they would.

When morning dawned the storm had passed, but not a fragment of the ship was to be seen. The sun rose red and shining above the water. The Prince's cheeks retained the hue of life, but his eyes were closed. The mermaid kissed his lofty handsome brow and stroked back his wet locks. He looked just like the marble statue down in her little garden; she kissed him again and wished that he might live.

And now she saw in front of her the mainland, the lofty blue mountains, on whose summits the snow shone as if it were swans that lay there; down on the shore were lovely green woods and right in front lay a church or cloister; she did not exactly know what it was, but it was a building of some sort. Lemon and orange trees grew in the garden, and before the gate stood tall palm trees. The sea had formed a little inlet here, calm but very deep, right up to the very cliff, near which the sea had washed up a beach of fine white sand. Thither the little mermaid swam with the handsome Prince and laid him on the sand, taking particular care that his head should lie high in the warm sunshine.

And now the bells in the large white building began ringing, and a number of young girls came walking through the garden. Then the little mermaid swam further out behind some lofty rocks which towered up out of the water, laying sea foam on her hair and breast so that no one might see her face, and watching to see who would come to the poor Prince.

It was not very long before a young girl came by that way; she appeared quite frightened when she saw him, but only for a moment. Then she went and brought a lot of people, and the mermaid saw that the Prince came to life again, and smiled on all around him, but he did not send a smile to her, for of course he did not know that she had saved him. She felt so grieved that when he was carried away into the large building she dived under the water and sorrowfully sought her father's palace.

She had always been silent and pensive, but now she became still more so. When her sisters asked her what she had seen up there the first time, she told them nothing. Many a morning and many an evening she ascended to the spot where she had seen the Prince. She saw how the fruits of the garden ripened and were plucked, she saw how the snow melted upon the lofty mountains, but the Prince she did not see, and therefore she returned home more and more sorrowful every time. Her only consolation was to sit in the little garden and wind her arms round the pretty marble statue which was so like the Prince. But she did not attend to her flowers at all; they grew wild, right over the paths, and wreathed their long stalks and leaves among the branches of the trees till it was quite gloomy there. At last she could endure her secret love no longer, but told it to one of her sisters, and so all the others immediately learned about it; but no one else knew it except a couple of other mermaids, who told it to nobody but their closest friends. One of these knew who the Prince was and all about him; she had also seen the merry-making on board the ship and knew whence he was and where his kingdom lay.

"Come, little sister!" said the other princesses, and with their arms around each other's shoulders they rose in a long row above the water in the place where they knew the Prince's palace lay. This palace was built of a light yellow glistening sort of stone with large marble staircases, one of which went straight down into the sea. Gorgeous gilded cupolas rose above the roof, and between the columns, which went round about the whole building, stood marble statues which looked like living beings. Through the clear glass in the lofty windows you looked into magnificent rooms hung with costly silk curtains and tapestries, and all the walls were adorned with large pictures, so that it was a pleasure to look at them. In the midst of the largest room splashed a large fountain, whose water-jets rose high toward the glass cupola, through which the sun shone upon the water and upon the beautiful plants which grew in the huge basin.

Now that the little mermaid knew where he dwelt, many an evening and night she rose upon the water there. She swam much nearer to the land than any of her sisters had ventured to do; nay, she went right up the narrow canal, beneath the magnificent marble balcony which cast a long shadow across the water. Here she used to sit and look at the Prince who thought himself alone in the bright moonshine.

Many an evening she saw him sail with music in his splendid boat where the banners waved; she peeped forth from the green rushes, and when the wind played with her long silvery white veil and people saw it, they fancied it was a swan lifting its wings.

Many a night when the fishermen were fishing by torchlight on the sea, she heard them speaking so well of the young Prince, that she was glad she had saved his life when he was drifting half dead upon the billows. She thought how his head had rested on her breast, and how ardently she then had kissed him; but as he knew nothing at all about it, he could not even dream of her.

And so she got to love human beings more and more, the more and more she desired to be among them. Their world seemed to her far grander than her own; why, they could sail across the sea in ships, ascend the lofty mountains high above the clouds, and call as their own lands that extended farther than her eye could reach. There was so much she would have liked to know, but her sisters would not answer everything she asked, and therefore she asked her old grandmother, for the Dowager knew all about the upper world, which she very correctly called the lands above the sea.

"When men don't drown," asked the little mermaid, "can they live forever? Don't they die as we do down in the sea here?"

"Yes," said the old grandmother, "they also must die; and indeed their life is even shorter than ours. We can last for three hundred years, but when at last we do cease to be, we become mere foam upon the water. We have not even a grave down here among our dear ones. We have no immortal soul; we never live again, we are like the green rushes, that—once they be cut down—cannot grow green again. Men on the other hand, have souls which always live— live when the body has become earth; they rise up through the clear air, right up to the shining stars; just as we rise out of the sea and see the lands of men, so they mount up to beautiful unknown places of which we shall never catch a glimpse."

"Why have we no immortal soul?" said the little mermaid sorrowfully. "I would give all the hundreds of years I have to live to be a human being but for a single day that so I might have my portion in the world above the sky!"

"You must not bother your head about that!" said the old grandmother. "We have a much better and happier lot than mankind up there."

"So I am to die and blow away like foam upon the sea, hear no more the music of the billows, see no more the pretty flowers and the red sun. Can I do nothing then at all to win an immortal soul?"

"No!" said the old grandmother, "only if a man were to love thee so dearly that thou wert more to him than father or mother, if he clave to thee with all his heart and soul, and let the priest lay his right hand in thine and vow fidelity to thee here and in all eternity, then his soul would flow over into thy body and thou wouldst have thy portion of human bliss. He would have given thee a soul, and yet have kept his own. But that can never be! The very thing that is so pretty in the sea here, thy fish's tail, is considered hideous upon earth. People don't know any better. Up there, to be thought handsome, one must have a couple of clumsy columns called legs!"

Then the little mermaid sighed and looked sorrowfully at her fish's tail.

"Let us be content with our lot," said the old grandmother. "We'll hop and skip about to our hearts' content in the three hundred years we have to live. Upon my word we have a nice long time of it. We'll have a court ball this very evening!"

And indeed it was a gorgeous sight such as one never sees on earth. The walls and ceiling of the vast dancing hall were of glass, thick but clear. Many hundreds of colossal shells, rosy-red and grass-green, stood in rows on each side full of a blue blazing fire which lit up the whole saloon and shone right through the walls so that the sea beyond them was illuminated. You could see all the countless fishes, both small and great, swimming towards the glass walls; the scales of some of them shone purple-red, the scales of others seemed like gold and silver. In the midst of the saloon flowed a broad running stream, and on this danced the mermen and the mermaids to their own pretty songs. Such lovely voices are unknown on earth.

The little mermaid sang sweetest of them all and they applauded her loudly, and for a moment her heart was glad, for she knew that she had the loveliest voice on the earth or in the sea. But very soon she began once more to think of the world above her; she could not forget the handsome Prince and her sorrow that unlike him, she had no immortal soul. So she stole quietly out of her father's palace, and while everything there was mirth and melody, she brooded in her little garden. Then she heard the bugle horn ringing down through the water, and she thought, "Now I know he is sailing up there, he whom I love more than father or mother, he to whom the thoughts of my heart cleave and in whose hands I would willingly lay my life's happiness. Everything will I venture to win him and an immortal soul! While my sisters are dancing within my father's palace, I will go to the sea witch; I have always been frightened of her, but she, perchance, may help and counsel me."

So the little mermaid went out of her own sea right toward the raging whirlpool behind which the witch dwelt. She had never gone that way before. No flowers, no sea grasses grew there, only the bare grey sandy bottom stretched out toward the whirlpools where the water like a rushing millwheel, whirled round and round, tearing everything it caught hold of away with it into the deep; she had to go right through the midst of these buffeting whirlpools to get to the sea witch's domain, and here, for a long stretch, there was no other way than across hot bubbling mire which the witch called her turf moss.

Right behind, lay her house in the midst of a strange wood. All the trees and bushes were polypi, half animal, half vegetable, they looked like hundred-headed serpents growing out of the earth; all their branches were long slimy arms with fingers like supple snakes, and joint by joint they were twisting and twirling from the roots to the outermost tips of their branches. Everything in the sea which they could catch hold of they wound themselves about and never let go of it again. The little Princess was terrified and remained standing outside there; her heart thumped for fear, she was very near turning back again, but then she thought of the Prince, and

143

of the human soul, and her courage came back to her.

She bound her long fluttering hair close to her head so that the polypi might not grasp it; then she crossed both hands over her breast, and away she flew through the water as only fishes can fly, right between the hideous polypi, stretching out their long supple arms and fingers after her. She saw that every one of them still had something which it had gripped, hundreds of little fingers held it like iron bands. Men who had perished in the sea and sunk down lay in arms of the polypi as white skeletons. Ships' rudders and coffers too they held fast; there were also the skeletons of land animals and even a little mermaid whom they had caught and tortured to death, and that was to her the most terrible sight of all.

And now she came to a large slimy open space in the wood where big fat water snakes were wallowing and airing their ugly whitey-yellow bellies. In the midst of the empty space a house had been raised from the white bones of shipwrecked men; here sat the Sea Witch and let a toad eat out of her mouth just as men let little canary birds pick sugar. She called the hideous fat water snakes her chicks and let them roll about over her large spongy bosom.

"I know well what you want!" said the Sea Witch. "You're a fool for your pains! Nevertheless you shall have your own way, for it will get you into trouble, my pretty Princess. You want to get rid of your fish's tail, eh? and have a couple of stumps to walk about on as men have, so that the young Prince may fall in love with you, and you may get him and an immortal soul into the bargain!" And with that, the witch laughed so loudly and hideously that the toad and the snakes fell down upon the ground and began wallowing there.

"You have come at the very nick of time," said the witch; "if you had put it off till tomorrow, at sunrise, I should not have been able to help you for another year. I'll brew you a potion, but you must swim to land, sit down on the shore, and drink it off before sunrise, and then your tail will split and shrivel up into what men call nice legs; but it will hurt, it will be like a sharp sword piercing through you. All who see you will say that you are the loveliest child of man they ever saw. You will keep your lightsome gait, no dancing girl will be able to float along like you; but every stride you take will be like treading on a sharp knife. If you can endure this, I'll help you."

"I will," said the mermaid with a trembling voice; she thought of the Prince and of winning an immortal soul.

"But remember this," said the witch. "When once you have a human shape you can never become a mermaid again! You can never again descend through the water to your sisters and to your father's palace, and if you do not win the Prince's love so that, for your sake, he forgets father and mother and cleaves to you with all his soul, and lets the priest lay your hands together and make you man and wife, you will get no immortal soul at all! The very first morning after he has married another, your heart will break and you will become foam upon the water!"

"Be it so!" said the little mermaid, but she was as pale as death.

"But you must pay me too," said the witch, "and it will not be a small thing either, that I demand. You have the loveliest voice of all things down below here at the bottom of the sea. You fancy you will enchant him with that, I know; not a bit of it. You must give that voice to me. I mean to have your best possession in return for my precious potion, for have I not to give you of my own blood in it, so that the potion may be as sharp as a two-edged sword?"

"But if you take my voice, what will be left for me?" asked the little mermaid.

"Your lovely shape," said the witch, "your lightsome gait and your speaking eye; you can fool a man's heart with them, I suppose? Well! have you lost heart, eh? Put out your little tongue and I'll cut it off in payment, and you shall have the precious potion!"

"Be it so, then!" said the little mermaid, and the witch put her kettle on to brew the magic potion. "Cleanliness is a good thing," said she, and she scoured out the cauldron with the snakes, which she tied into a knot; then she gashed herself in the breast and let her black blood drip down into the cauldron. The steam that rose from it took the strangest shapes, so that one could not but feel anguish and terror. Every moment the witch put something fresh into the cauldron, and when it was well on the boil it sounded like a crying crocodile. At last the drink was ready. It looked like the clearest water!

"There you are!" said the witch, and she cut out the tongue of the little mermaid who was now quite dumb; she could neither sing nor talk.

"If the polypi grip at you when you go back through the wood," said the witch, "just you throw a single drop of this potion upon them, and their arms and fingers will burst into a thousand bits!" But the mermaid had no need to do this; the polypi shrank back from her in terror when they saw the shining potion that sparkled in her hand like a dazzling star. So very soon she got through the wood, the morass and the raging whirlpool. She could see her father's palace; the lights in the long dancing hall had been put out; all within there were doubtless sleeping; but she dared not venture to visit them now that she was dumb, and was to go away from them forever. Yet her heart felt as if it must burst asunder for sorrow.

She crept down into the garden, plucked a flower from each of her sister's flowerbeds, threw a thousand kisses towards the palace, and ascended again through the dark blue sea. The sun had not yet risen when she beheld the Prince's palace, and mounted the splendid marble staircase. The moon was shining bright and beautiful. The little mermaid drank the sharp burning potion, and it was as though a two-edged sword pierced right through her body; she moaned with the agony and lay there as one dead.

When the sun shone over the sea she woke up and felt a sharp pang, but before her stood the handsome young Prince. He fixed his coal-black eyes upon her, so that she cast her own eyes down and saw that her fish tail had gone, and that she had the prettiest slim white legs. But as she was quite naked, she wrapped herself in her long locks. The Prince asked who she was and how she came thither; and she looked at him with her dark blue eyes tenderly and yet sadly, for speak she could not. Then he took her by the hand and led her into his palace. Every step she took was, as the witch had warned that it would be, as if she were treading on pointed awls or sharp

146

knives, but she willingly bore it. Holding the Prince's hand, she mounted the staircase as light as a bubble, and he and everyone else were amazed at her graceful, lightsome gait. Once she was arrayed in the most costly garments, all silk and satin, none in the whole palace was so lovely as she; but she was dumb, she could neither sing nor speak. Lovely slave girls, clad in silk and gold, came forth and sang to the Prince and his royal parents; one of them sang more sweetly than all the rest, and the Prince clapped his hands and smiled at her. Then the little mermaid was troubled; she knew that she herself had sung far more sweetly, and she thought: "Oh, would that he might know that for the sake of being near him, I have given away my voice forever and ever!"

And now the slave girls danced the graceful, lightsome dance to the loveliest music, and then the little mermaid raised on high her lovely white arms, raised herself on the tips of her toes, and danced and swept across the floor as none ever danced before; at every movement her loveliness became more and more visible and her eyes spoke more deeply to the heart than ever the songs of the slave girl. They were all enchanted with her, especially the Prince, who called her his little foundling, and she danced more and more, though every time her feet touched the ground it was as if she trod upon a sharp knife. The Prince said she should always be with him, and gave her leave to sit outside his door on a velvet cushion.

He had a page boy's costume made for her that she might ride out with him. They rode through the fragrant woods where the green branches smote her on the shoulders and the little birds sang behind the fresh leaves. She clambered with the Prince right up the high mountains and although her tender feet bled, so that the others could see it, she only laughed and followed him till they saw the clouds sailing below them like flocks of birds departing to a foreign land.

At night, in the Prince's palace, while others slept, she went out upon the broad marble staircase, and it cooled her burning feet to stand in the cold sea water, and then she thought of her family in the depths below.

One night her sisters came up arm in arm. They sang so sorrowfully as they swam in the water, and she nodded to them, and they recognized her, and told her how miserable she had made them all. After that, they visited her every night, and one night she saw, a long way out, her old grandmother who had not been above the sea for many years, and the Sea King with his crown upon his head; they stretched out their hands towards her, but dared not come so close to land as her sisters.

She became dearer to the Prince every day. He loved her as one might love a dear, good child; but to make her his queen never entered his mind. Yet his wife she must be, or she would never have an immortal soul, but would turn into sea foam upon his bridal morn.

"Do you love me most of all?" the eyes of the little mermaid seemed to say when he took her in his arms and kissed her fair brow.

"Yes, you are dearest of all to me," said the Prince, "for you have the best heart of them all, you are most devoted to me, and you are just like a young girl I once saw but certainly shall never see again. I was on a ship which was wrecked; the billows drifted me ashore near a holy temple, where many young girls were the ministrants. The youngest, who found me on the seashore and saved my life, I only saw twice; she is the only girl I can love in this world, but you are like her. You almost drive her image from my soul; she belongs to that holy temple, and therefore my good fortune has sent me you instead, we will never part!"

"Alas! he knows not that 'twas I who saved his life!" thought the little mermaid. "I bore him right over the sea to the wood where the temple stands, I sat behind the foam and looked to see if any one would come; I saw the pretty girl whom he loves better than me!" And the mermaid drew a deep sigh, weep she could not. "He says the girl belongs to that holy temple, she will never come forth into the world, they will never meet again. I am with him, I see him every day, I will cherish him, love him, sacrifice my life for him."

But now the Prince was to be married and take the lovely daughter of the neighboring king to wife, and that was why he set about equipping a splendid ship. The Prince is traveling to see the land of

148

the neighboring king, everyone said; but it was to see the neighboring king's daughter that he went forth with such a grand retinue. The little mermaid shook her head and laughed; she knew the Prince's thoughts much better than all the others. "I must travel," he had said to her, "I must see the fair Princess, my parents require it of me; but they shall not compel me to bring her home as my bride. I cannot love her, she is not like the lovely girl in the temple whom you are like. Should I ever choose me a bride, it would rather be you, my dumb foundling with the speaking eyes!" And he kissed her red mouth, played with her long hair, and laid his head close to her heart till her heart dreamed of human bliss and an immortal soul.

"Surely you are not frightened at the sea, mute child!" said he, as they stood on the gorgeous ship which was to carry him to the land of the neighboring king; and he told her about storm and calm, about the strange fishes of the deep, and what the divers had seen down there, and she smiled at his telling, for she knew better than any one else all about the bottom of the sea.

In the moonlight nights when all were asleep save the man at the helm, she sat at the side of the ship and looked down through the clear water and seemed to see her father's palace, and at the very top of it stood the old grandmother with the silver crown upon her head, and stared up at the ship's keel through the contrary currents. Then her sisters came up to the surface of the water; they gazed sadly at her and wrung their white hands. She beckoned to them, smiled, and would have told them that everything was going on well and happily, but the cabin boy drew near at that moment and her sisters dropped down again, so that she half fancied that the white things she had seen were the foam upon the sea.

The next morning the ship sailed into the haven of the neighboring king's splendid capital. All the church bells were ringing, bassoons sounded from the tops of the high towers, while the soldiers stood drawn up with waving banners and flashing bayonets. Every day had its own special feast. Balls and assemblies followed each other in rapid succession, but the Princess was not yet there. She had been brought up in a holy temple far away, they said, where she had learned all royal virtues. At last she arrived.

Full of eagerness the little mermaid stood there to see her loveliness; and recognize it she must. A more beauteous shape she had never seen. Her skin was so transparently fine, and from behind the long dark eyelashes smiled a pair of dark blue, faithful eyes.

" 'Tis thou!" said the Prince, "thou who hast saved me when I lay like a corpse on the seashore!" and he embraced his blushing bride. "I am happy beyond all reckoning!" said he to the little mermaid. "The very best I dared to hope has come to pass. You too will rejoice at my good fortune, for you love me more than them all!" The little mermaid kissed his hand, but she felt that her heart was like to break. Yes, his bridal morn would be her death, and change her into sea foam.

All the bells were ringing, and the heralds rode about the streets to proclaim the espousals.

Fragrant oil in precious silver lamps burned upon every altar. The priests swung their censers, and the bride and bridegroom gave each other their hands and received the bishop's benediction. In cloth of gold, the little mermaid held the bride's train, but her ears did not hear the festal music, her eyes did not see the sacred ceremony; she thought of her night of death; she thought of all she had lost in this world.

The same evening the bride and bridegroom went on board the ship, the cannons were fired, all the flags waved, and in the midst of the ship a royal tent was raised of cloth of gold and purple and precious furs; there the bridal pair were to sleep in the still, cool night.

The sails swelled out in the breeze, and the ship glided, lightly rocking, away over the bright ocean. When it grew dark, colored lamps were lit, and the mariners danced merry dances on the deck. The little mermaid could not help thinking of the first time she had come up above the sea, and had seen the self-same gaiety and splendor. She whirled round and round in the dance, skimming along as the swallow skims when it is pursued, and everyone applauded her enthusiastically. Never before had she danced so splendidly. There was a piercing as of sharp knives in her feet, but she felt it not; the anguish of her heart was far more piercing. She knew this was the last evening she was to see him for whom she had forsaken house and home, surrendered her lovely voice, and suffered endless tortures day by day, without his having any idea of it all. This was the last night she was to breathe the same air as he, and look upon the deep sea and the star-lit sky. An eternal night without a thought, without a dream, awaited her who had no soul and could not win one. All was joy and jollity on board the ship till long past midnight, and she laughed and danced with the thought of death in her heart. The Prince kissed his lovely bride, and she toyed with his black hair, and arm in arm they went to rest in the gorgeous tent.

It grew dark and still on board; only the steersman was there, standing at the helm. The little mermaid laid her white arms on the railing and looked towards the east for the rosy dawn. The first sunbeam, she knew well, must kill her. Then she saw her sisters rise up from the sea. They were as pale as she was; their long fair hair fluttered no longer in the breeze; it was all cut off.

"We have given it to the witch that she might bring help so that you may not die tonight! She has given us a knife. Here it is. Look how sharp it is! Before the sun rises you must thrust it into the Prince's heart, and then, when his warm blood sprinkles your feet, they will grow together into a fish's tail, and you will become a mermaid again, and may sink down through the water to us, and live out your three hundred years before you become sea foam. But hasten! Either you or he must die before sunrise. Our old grandmother has sorrowed so that her hair has fallen off, just as ours has fallen off beneath the witch's shears. Kill the Prince and come back to us! Hasten! Don't you see the red strip in the sky yonder? A few minutes more and the sun will rise and you must die." And they heaved a wondrously deep sigh and sank beneath the billows.

The little mermaid drew aside the purple curtains from the tent door. She saw the beauteous bride sleeping with her head on the Prince's breast. She bent down and kissed him on his fair brow. She

151

looked at the sky where the red dawn shone brighter and brighter, looked at the sharp knife, and again fixed her eyes on the Prince, who, in his dreams, named his wife by her name, for she alone was in his thoughts. The knife quivered in the mermaid's hand—but then she cast it out far into the billows. They shone red where it fell, as if drops of blood were there bubbling up out of the water. Once again she looked at the Prince; then she plunged from the ship into the sea, and her whole body dissolved into foam.

And now the sun rose out of the sea. His rays fell with so gentle a warmth upon the death-cold sea foam, that the little mermaid did not feel death; she saw the bright sun, and right above her hundreds of beauteous, transparent shapes were hovering. Through them she could see the white sails of the ship and the red clouds of the sky. Their voices were all melody, but so ethereal that no human ear could hear it, just as no human eye could see them; they had no wings, but their very lightness wafted them up and down in the air. The little mermaid saw that she had a body like them. It rose higher and higher out of the foam. "To whom have I come?" said she, and her voice sounded like the voices of the other beings, more beautiful than earthly music.

"To the daughters of the air," answered the others, "the mermaid has no immortal soul and can never have one unless she wins a man's love. Her eternal existence depends upon a Power beyond her. The daughters of the air, likewise, have no immortal soul, but they can make themselves one by good deeds. We fly to the hot countries, where the sultry, pestilential air slays the children of men; there we waft coolness. We spread the fragrance of flowers through the air and send refreshment and healing. When for three hundred years we have striven to do all the good we can, we get an immortal soul and have a share in the eternal destinies of mankind. Thou, poor little mermaid, thou also hast striven after good with thy whole heart; like us, thou hast suffered and endured, and raised thyself into the sphere of the spirits of the air; now therefore, thou canst also win for thyself an immortal soul after three hundred years of good deeds."

And the little mermaid raised her bright arms towards God's sun, and for the first time she felt tears in her eyes. There was life and bustle on board the ship again. She saw the Prince with his fair bride looking for her, and they gazed sadly down upon the bubbling foam, as if they knew she had plunged into the billows. Invisible as she was, she kissed the bride's brow, smiled upon the Prince, and ascended with the other children of the air to the rosy red clouds which were sailing along in the sky. "For three hundred years we shall float and float till we float right into God's kingdom."

"Yea, and we may also get there still sooner," whispered one of them. "Invisibly we sweep into the houses of men, where there are children, and every day we find there a good child who gladdens his parents' hearts and deserves their love, God shortens our time of trial. The child does not know when we fly through the room, but when we can smile with joy over it, a whole year is taken from off the three hundred; but whenever we see a bad, naughty child, we must, perforce, weep tears of sorrow, and every tear adds a day to our time of trial!"

The Forsaken Merman

MATTHEW ARNOLD

Come dear children, let us away;
Down and away below.
Now my brothers call from the bay;
Now the great winds shoreward blow;
Now the salt tides seaward flow;
Now the wild white horses play,
Champ and chafe and toss in the spray.
   Children dear, let us away.
     This way, this way!

Call her once before you go.
    Call once yet.
In a voice that she will know:
  "Margaret! Margaret!"

Children's voices should be dear
(Call once more) to a mother's ear;
Children's voices, wild with pain.
Surely she will come again.
Call her once and come away.
        This way, this way!
"Mother dear, we cannot stay."
    The wild horses foam and fret.
        "Margaret! Margaret!"

Come, dear children, come away down.
        Call no more.
One last look at the white-wall'd town,
And the little grey church on the windy shore.
        Then come down.
She will not come though you call all day.
        Come away, come away.

Children dear, was it yesterday
We heard the sweet bells over the bay?
In the caverns where we lay,
Through the surf and through the swell,
The far-off sound of a silver bell?
Sand-strewn caverns, cool and deep,
Where the winds are still asleep;
Where the spent lights quiver and gleam;
Where the salt weed sways in the stream;
Where the sea-beasts, ranged all round,
Feed in the ooze of their pasture ground;
Where the sea snakes coil and twine,
Dry their mail, and bask in the brine;
Where great whales come sailing by,
Sail and sail, with unshut eye,
Round the world for ever and aye?

When did music come this way?
Children dear, was it yesterday?

Children dear, was it yesterday
(Call yet once) that she went away?
Once she sate with you and me,
On a red gold throne in the heart of the sea,
And the youngest sate on her knee.
She combed its bright hair, and she tended it well,
When down swung the sound of the far-off bell.
She sigh'd, she look'd up through the clear green sea.
She said, "I must go, for my kinsfolk pray
In the little grey church on the shore today.
'Twill be Easter time in the world—ah me!
And I lose my poor soul, Merman, here with thee."
I said, "Go up, dear heart, through the waves.
Say thy prayer, and come back to the kind sea caves,"
She smiled, she went up through the surf in the bay.
Children dear, was it yesterday?

Children dear, were we long alone?
"The sea grows stormy," the little ones moan.
"Long prayers," I said, "in the world they say.
Come," I said, and we rose through the surf in the bay.
We went up the beach, by the sandy down
Where the sea stocks bloom, to the white-wall'd town.
Through the narrow paved streets, where all was still,
To the little grey church on the windy hill.
From the church came a murmur of folk at their prayers,
But we stood without in the cold blowing airs.
We climbed on the graves, on the stones worn with rains,
And we gazed up the aisle through the small leaded panes.
She sate by the pillar; we saw her clear
"Margaret, hist! come quick, we are here.
Dear heart," I said, "we are long alone.

The sea grows stormy, the little ones moan."
But ah! she gave me never a look,
For her eyes were seal'd to the holy book.
Loud prays the priest; shut stands the door.
    Come away, children, call no more.
    Come away, come down, call no more.

    Down, down, down;
    Down to the depths of the sea.
She sits at her wheel in the humming town,
    Singing most joyfully.
Hark what she sings: "O joy, O joy,
For the humming street, and the child with its toy.
For the priest, and the bell, and the holy well.
    For the wheel where I spun,
    And the blessed light of the sun"
And so she sings her fill,
    Singing most joyfully,
    Till the shuttle falls from her hand,
    And the whizzing wheel stands still.
She steals to the window, and looks at the sand;
    And over the sand at the sea;
    And her eyes are set in a stare;
    And anon there breaks a sigh,
    And anon there drops a tear,
    From a sorrow-clouded eye,
    And a heart sorrow-laden,
      A long, long sigh
For the cold strange eyes of a little Mermaiden,
    And the gleam of her golden hair.

Come away, away, children.
Come children, come down.
The hoarse wind blows colder;
Lights shine in the town.

She will start from her slumber
When gusts shake the door;
She will hear the winds howling,
Will hear the waves roar.
We shall see, while above us
The waves roar, and whirl,
A ceiling of amber,
A pavement of pearl.
Singing, "Here came a mortal,
But faithless was she:
And alone dwell for ever
The kings of the sea."

But, children, at midnight,
When soft the winds blow;
When clear falls the moonlight;
When spring tides are low:
When sweet airs come seaward
From heaths starr'd with broom;
And high rocks throw mildly
On the blanch'd sands a gloom:
Up the still, glistening beaches,
Up the creeks we will hie;
Over banks of bright seaweed
The ebb tide leaves dry.
We will gaze, from the sand hills,
At the white, sleeping town;
At the church on the hillside——
    And then come back down.
Singing, "There dwells a loved one,
    But cruel is she.
She left lonely for ever
    The kings of the sea."

The Fisherman
and his Soul

OSCAR WILDE

EVERY evening the young Fisherman went out upon the sea, and threw his nets into the water.

When the wind blew from the land he caught nothing, or little at best, for it was a bitter and black-winged wind, and rough waves rose up to meet it. But when the wind blew to the shore, the fish came in from the deep, and swam into the meshes of his nets, and he took them to the marketplace and sold them.

Every evening he went out upon the sea, and one evening the net was so heavy that hardly could he draw it into the boat. And

159

he laughed, and said to himself, "Surely I have caught all the fish that swim, or snared some dull monster that will be a marvel to men, or some thing of horror that the great Queen will desire." And putting forth all his strength, he tugged at the coarse ropes till, like lines of blue enamel round a vase of bronze, the long veins rose up on his arms. He tugged at the thin ropes, and nearer and nearer came the circle of flat corks, and the net rose at last to the top of the water.

But no fish at all was in it, nor any monster or thing of horror, but only a little Mermaid lying fast asleep.

Her hair was a wet fleece of gold, and each separate hair as a thread of fine gold in a cup of glass. Her body was as white ivory, and her tail was of silver and pearl. Silver and pearl was her tail, and the green weeds of the sea coiled round it; and like seashells were her ears, and her lips were like sea coral. The cold waves dashed over her cold breasts, and the salt glistened upon her eyelids.

So beautiful was she that when the young Fisherman saw her, he was filled with wonder, and he put out his hand and drew the net close to him, and leaning over the side he clasped her in his arms. And when he touched her, she gave a cry like a startled sea gull and woke, and looked at him in terror with her mauve-amethyst eyes, and struggled that she might escape. But he held her tightly to him and would not suffer her to depart.

And when she saw that she could in no way escape from him, she began to weep and said, "I pray thee let me go, for I am the only daughter of a King, and my father is aged and alone."

But the young Fisherman answered, "I will not let thee go save thou makest me a promise that whenever I call thee, thou wilt come and sing to me, for the fish delight to listen to the song of the Sea-folk, and so shall my nets be full."

"Wilt thou in very truth let me go, if I promise thee this?" cried the Mermaid.

"In very truth I will let thee go," said the young Fisherman. So she made him the promise he desired, and swore it by the oath of the Sea-folk. And he loosened his arms from about her, and she sank down into the water, trembling with a strange fear.

Every evening the young Fisherman went out upon the sea and called to the Mermaid, and she rose out of the water and sang to him. Round and round her swam the dolphins, and the wild gulls wheeled above her head.

And she sang a marvellous song. For she sang of the Sea-folk who drive their flocks from cave to cave, and carry the little calves on their shoulders; of the Tritons who have long green beards, and hairy breasts, and blow through twisted conches when the King passes by; of the palace of the King which is all of amber, with a roof of clear emerald, and a pavement of bright pearl; and of the gardens of the sea where the great filigrane fans of coral wave all day long, and the fish dart about like silver birds, and the anemones cling to the rocks, and the pinks bourgeon in the ribbed yellow sand. She sang of the big whales that come down from the north seas and have sharp icicles hanging to their fins; of the Sirens who tell of such wonderful things that the merchants have to stop their ears with wax lest they should hear them, and leap into the water and be drowned; of the sunken galleys with their tall masts, and the frozen sailors clinging to the rigging, and the mackerel swimming in and out of the open portholes; of the little barnacles who are great travellers, and cling to the keels of the ships and go round and round the world; and of the cuttlefish who live in the sides of the cliffs and stretch out their long black arms, and can make night come when they will it. She sang of the nautilus who has a boat of her own that is carved out of an opal and steered with a silken sail; of the happy Mermen who play upon harps and can charm the great Kraken to sleep; of the little children who catch hold of the slippery porpoises and ride laughing upon their backs; of the Mermaids who lie in the white foam and hold out their arms to the mariners; and of the sea lions with their curved tusks, and the sea horses with their floating manes.

And as she sang, all the tunnyfish came in from the deep to listen to her, and the young Fisherman threw his nets round them and caught them, and others he took with a spear. And when his boat was well-laden, the Mermaid would sink down into the sea, smiling at him.

Yet would she never come near him that he might touch her. Oftentimes he called to her and prayed of her, but she would not; and when he sought to seize her she dived into the water as a seal might dive, nor did he see her again that day. And each day the sound of her voice became sweeter to his ears. So sweet was her voice that he forgot his nets and his cunning, and had no care of his craft. Vermilion-finned and with eyes of bossy gold, the tunnies went by in shoals, but he heeded them not. His spear lay by his side unused, and his baskets of plaited osier were empty. With lips parted, and eyes dim with wonder, he sat idle in his boat and listened, listened till the sea mists crept round him, and the wandering moon stained his brown limbs with silver.

And one evening he called to her, and said, "Little Mermaid, little Mermaid, I love thee. Take me for thy bridegroom for I love thee."

But the Mermaid shook her head. "Thou hast a human soul," she answered. "If only thou wouldst send away thy soul, then could I love thee."

And the young Fisherman said to himself, "Of what use is my soul to me? I cannot see it. I may not touch it. I do not know it. Surely I will send it away from me, and much gladness shall be mine." And a cry of joy broke from his lips, and standing up in the painted boat, he held out his arms to the Mermaid. "I will send away my soul," he cried, "and you shall be my bride, and I will be thy bridegroom, and in the depth of the sea we will dwell together, and all that thou hast sung of thou shalt show me, and all that thou desirest I will do, nor shall our lives be divided."

And the little Mermaid laughed for pleasure and hid her face in her hands.

"But how shall I send my soul from me?" cried the young Fisherman. "Tell me how I may do it, and lo! it shall be done."

"Alas! I know not," said the little Mermaid, "the Sea-folk have no souls." And she sank down into the deep, looking wistfully at him.

Now early on the next morning, before the sun was the span of a man's hand above the hill, the young Fisherman went to the house of the Priest and knocked three times at the door.

The novice looked out through the wicket, and when he saw who it was, he drew back the latch and said to him, "Enter."

And the young Fisherman passed in, and knelt down on the sweet-smelling rushes of the floor, and cried to the Priest who was reading out of the Holy Book and said to him, "Father, I am in love with one of the Sea-folk, and my soul hindereth me from having my desire. Tell me how I can send my soul away from me, for in truth I have no need of it. Of what value is my soul to me? I cannot see it. I may not touch it. I do not know it."

And the Priest beat his breast, and answered, "Alack, alack, thou art mad, or hast eaten of some poisonous herb, for the soul is the noblest part of man, and was given to us by God that we should nobly use it. There is no thing more precious than a human soul, nor any earthly thing that can be weighed with it. It is worth all the gold that is in the world, and is more precious than the rubies of the kings. Therefore, my son, think not any more of this matter, for it is a sin that may not be forgiven. And as for the Sea-folk, they are lost, and they who would traffic with them are lost also. They are the beasts of the field that know not good from evil, and for them the Lord has not died."

The young Fisherman's eyes filled with tears when he heard the bitter words of the Priest, and he rose up from his knees and said to him, "Father, the Fauns live in the forest and are glad, and on the rocks sit the Mermen with their harps of red-gold. Let me be as they are, I beseech thee, for their days are as the days of flowers. And as for my soul, what doth my soul profit me, if it stand between me and the thing I love?"

"The love of the body is vile," cried the Priest, knitting his brows, "and vile and evil are the pagan things God suffers to wander through His world. Accursed be the Fauns of the woodland and accursed be the singers of the sea! I have heard them at night-time, and they have sought to lure me from my beads. They tap at the window and laugh. They whisper into my ears the tale of their perilous joys. They tempt me with temptations, and when I would pray they make mouths at me. They are lost, I tell thee, they are lost. For them there is no heaven nor hell, and in neither shall they praise God's name."

"Father," cried the Fisherman, "thou knowest not what thou sayest. Once in my net I snared the daughter of a King. She is fairer than the morning star, and whiter than the moon. For her body I would give my soul, and for her love I would surrender heaven. Tell me what I ask of thee, and let me go in peace."

"Away! Away!" cried the Priest, "thy leman is lost, and thou shalt be lost with her." And he gave him no blessing, but drove him from his door.

And the young Fisherman went down into the market-place, and he walked slowly, and with bowed head, as one who is in sorrow.

And when the merchants saw him coming, they began to whisper to each other, and one of them came forth to meet him, and called him by name, and said to him, "What hast thou to sell?"

"I will sell thee my soul," he answered. "I pray thee buy it of me, for I am weary of it. Of what use is my soul to me? I cannot see it. I may not touch it. I do not know it."

But the merchants mocked at him, and said, "Of what use is a man's soul to us? It is not worth a clipped piece of silver. Sell us thy body for a slave, and we will clothe thee in sea-purple, and put a ring upon thy finger, and make thee the minion of the great Queen. But talk not of the soul, for to us it is nought, nor has it any value for our service."

And the young Fisherman said to himself: "How strange a thing this is! The Priest telleth me that the soul is worth all the gold in the world, and the merchants say that it is not worth a clipped piece of silver." And he passed out of the market-place, and went down to the shore of the sea, and began to ponder on what he should do.

And at noon he remembered how one of his companions, who was a gatherer of samphire, had told him of a certain young Witch who dwelt in a cave at the head of the bay and was very cunning in her witcheries. And he set to and ran, so eager was he to get rid of his soul, and a cloud of dust followed him as he sped round the sand of the shore. By the itching of her palm the young Witch knew his coming, and she laughed and let down her red hair. With her red hair falling around her, she stood at the opening of the cave, and in her hand she had a spray of wild hemlock that was blossoming.

"What d'ye lack? What d'ye lack?" she cried, as he came panting up the steep, and bent down before her. "Fish for thy net, when the wind is foul? I have a little reed pipe, and when I blow on it the mullet come sailing into the bay. But it has a price, pretty boy, it has a price. What d'ye lack? What d'ye lack? A storm to wreck the ships, and wash the chests of rich treasure ashore? I have more storms than the wind has, for I serve one who is stronger than the wind, and with a sieve and a pail of water I can send the great galleys to the bottom of the sea. But I have a price, pretty boy, I have a price. What d'ye lack? What d'ye lack? I know a flower that grows in the valley, none knows it but I. It has purple leaves, and a star in its heart, and its juice is as white as milk. Shouldst thou touch with this flower the hard lips of the Queen, she would follow thee all over the world. Out of the bed of the King she would rise, and over the whole world she would follow thee. And it has a price, pretty boy, it has a price. What d'ye lack? What d'ye lack? I can pound a toad in a mortar, and make broth of it, and stir the broth with a dead man's hand. Sprinkle it on thine enemy while he sleeps, and he will turn into a black viper, and his own mother will slay him. With a wheel I can draw the Moon from heaven, and in a crystal I can show thee Death. What d'ye lack? What d'ye lack? Tell me thy desire, and I will give it thee, and thou shalt pay me a price, pretty boy, thou shalt pay me a price."

"My desire is but for a little thing," said the young Fisherman, "yet hath the Priest been wroth with me, and driven me forth. It is but for a little thing, and the merchants have mocked at me, and denied me. Therefore am I come to thee, though men call thee evil, and what ever be thy price I shall pay it."

"What wouldst thou?" asked the Witch, coming near to him.

"I would send my soul away from me," answered the young Fisherman.

The Witch grew pale, and shuddered, and hid her face in her

blue mantle. "Pretty boy, pretty boy," she muttered, "that is a terrible thing to do."

He tossed his brown curls and laughed. "My soul is nought to me," he answered. "I cannot see it. I may not touch it. I do not know it."

"What wilt thou give me if I tell thee?" asked the Witch, looking down at him with her beautiful eyes.

"Five pieces of gold," he said, "and my nets, and the wattled house where I live, and the painted boat in which I sail. Only tell me how to get rid of my soul, and I will give thee all that I possess."

She laughed mockingly at him, and struck him with the spray of hemlock. "I can turn the autumn leaves into gold," she answered, "and I can weave the pale moonbeams into silver if I will it. He whom I serve is richer than all the kings of this world, and has their dominions."

"What then shall I give thee," he cried, "if thy price be neither gold nor silver."

The Witch stroked his hair with her thin white hand. "Thou must dance with me, pretty boy," she murmured, and she smiled at him as she spoke.

"Nought but that?" cried the young Fisherman in wonder, and he rose to his feet.

"Nought but that," she answered, and she smiled at him again.

"Then at sunset in some secret place we shall dance together," he said, "and after we have danced thou shalt tell me the thing which I desire to know."

She shook her head. "When the moon is full, when the moon is full," she muttered. Then she peered all round, and listened. A blue bird rose screaming from its nest and circled over the dunes, and three spotted birds rustled through the coarse grey grass and whistled to each other. There was no other sound save the sound of a wave fretting the smooth pebbles below. So she reached out her hand, and drew him near to her and put her dry lips close to his ear.

"Tonight thou must come to the top of the mountain," she whispered. "It is a Sabbath, and He will be there."

The young Fisherman started and looked at her, and she showed her white teeth and laughed. "Who is He of whom thou speakest?" he asked.

"It matters not," she answered. "Go thou tonight, and stand under the branches of the hornbeam, and wait for my coming. If a black dog run towards thee, strike it with a rod of willow, and it will go away. If an owl speak to thee, make it no answer. When the moon is full I shall be with thee, and we will dance together on the grass."

"But wilt thou swear to me to tell me how I may send my soul from me?" he made question.

She moved out into the sunlight, and through her red hair rippled the wind. "By the hoofs of the goat I swear it," she made answer.

"Thou art the best of the witches," cried the young Fisherman, "and I will surely dance with thee tonight on the top of the mountain. I would indeed that thou hadst asked of me either gold or silver. But such as thy price is thou shalt have it, for it is but a little thing." And he doffed his cap to her, and bent his head low, and ran back to the town filled with a great joy.

And the Witch watched him as he went, and when he had passed from her sight she entered her cave, and having taken a mirror from a box of carved cedarwood, she set it up on a frame, and burned vervain on lighted charcoal before it, and peered through the coils of the smoke. And after a time she clenched her hands in anger. "He should have been mine," she muttered, "I am as fair as she is."

And that evening, when the moon had risen, the young Fisherman climbed up to the top of the mountain, and stood under the branches of the hornbeam. Like a shield of polished metal the round sea lay at his feet, and the shadows of the fishing boats moved in the little bay. A great owl, with yellow sulphurous eyes, called to him by his name, but he made no answer. A black dog ran towards him and snarled. He struck it with a rod of willow, and it went away whining.

At midnight the witches came flying through the air like bats.

"Phew!" they cried, as they lit upon the ground. "There is some-one here we know not!" and they sniffed about, and chattered to each other, and made signs. Last of all came the young Witch, with her red hair streaming in the wind. She wore a dress of gold tissue embroidered with peacocks' eyes, and a little cap of green velvet was on her head.

"Where is he, where is he?" shrieked the witches when they saw her, but she only laughed and ran to the hornbeam, and taking the Fisherman by the hand she led him out into the moonlight and began to dance.

Round and round they whirled, and the young Witch jumped so high that he could see the scarlet heels of her shoes. Then right across the dancers came the sound of the galloping of a horse, but no horse was to be seen, and he felt afraid.

"Faster," cried the Witch, and she threw her arms about his neck, and her breath was hot upon his face. "Faster, faster!" she cried, and the earth seemed to spin beneath his feet, and his brain grew troubled, and a great terror fell on him, as of some evil thing that was watching him, and at last he became aware that under the shadow of a rock there was a figure that had not been there before.

It was a man dressed in a suit of black velvet, cut in the Spanish fashion. His face was strangely pale, but his lips were like a proud red flower. He seemed weary, and was leaning back toying in a listless manner with the pommel of his dagger. On the grass beside him lay a plumed hat, and a pair of riding gloves, gauntleted with gilt lace and sewn with seed pearls wrought into a curious device. A short cloak lined with sables hung from his shoulder, and his delicate white hands were gemmed with rings. Heavy eyelids drooped over his eyes.

The young Fisherman watched him, as one snared in a spell. At last their eyes met, and wherever he danced it seemed to him that the eyes of the man were upon him. He heard the Witch laugh, and caught her by the waist, and whirled her madly round and round.

Suddenly a dog bayed in the wood, and the dancers stopped, and going up two by two, knelt down, and kissed the man's hands. As they did so, a little smile touched his proud lips, as a bird's wing touches the water and makes it laugh. But there was disdain in it. He kept looking at the young Fisherman.

"Come! let us worship," whispered the Witch, and she led him up, and a great desire to do as she besought him seized on him, and he followed her. But when he came close, and without knowing why he did it, he made on his breast the sign of the Cross, and called upon the Holy Name.

No sooner had he done so than the witches screamed like hawks and flew away, and the pallid face that had been watching him twitched with a spasm of pain. The man went over to a little wood, and whistled. A jennet with silver trappings came running to meet him. As he leapt upon the saddle he turned round, and looked at the young Fisheman sadly.

And the Witch with the red hair tried to fly away also, but the Fisherman caught her by her wrists, and held her fast.

"Loose me," she cried, "and let me go. For thou hast named what should not be named, and shown the sign that may not be looked at."

"Nay," he answered, "but I will not let thee go till thou hast told me the secret."

"What secret?" said the Witch, wrestling with him like a wild cat, and biting her foam-flecked lips.

"Thou knowest," he made answer.

Her grass-green eyes grew dim with tears, and she said to the Fisherman, "Ask me anything but that!"

He laughed, and held her all the more tightly.

And when she saw that she could not free herself, she whispered to him, "Surely I am as fair as the daughter of the sea, and as comely as those that dwell in the blue waters," and she fawned on him and put her face close to his.

But he thrust her back frowning, and said to her, "If thou keepest not the promise that thou madest to me I will slay thee for a false witch."

She grew grey as a blossom of the Judas tree, and shuddered.

"Be it so," she muttered. "It is thy soul and not mine. Do with it as

169

thou wilt." And she took from her girdle a little knife that had a handle of green viper skin, and gave it to him.

"What shall this serve me?" he asked of her, wondering.

She was silent for a few moments, and a look of terror came over her face. Then she brushed her hair back from her forehead, and smiling strangely she said to him, "What men call the shadow of the body is not the shadow of the body, but is the body of the soul. Stand on the seashore with thy back to the moon, and cut away from around thy feet thy shadow, which is thy soul's body, and bid thy soul leave thee, and it will do so."

The young Fisherman trembled. "Is this true?" he murmured.

"It is true, and I would that I had not told thee of it," she cried and she clung to his knees weeping.

He put her from him and left her in the rank grass, and going to the edge of the mountain he placed the knife in his belt and began to climb down.

And his Soul that was within him called out to him and said, "Lo! I have dwelt with thee for all these years, and have been thy servant. Send me not away from thee now, for what evil have I done thee?"

And the young Fisherman laughed. "Thou hast done me no evil, but I have no need of thee," he answered. "The world is wide, and there is Heaven also, and Hell, and that dim twilight house that lies between. Go wherever thou wilt, but trouble me not for my love is calling to me."

And his Soul besought him piteously, but he heeded it not, but leapt from crag to crag, being as sure-footed as a wild goat, and at last he reached the level ground and the yellow shore of the sea.

Bronze-limbed and well-knit, like a statue wrought by a Grecian, he stood on the sand with his back to the moon, and out of the foam came white arms that beckoned to him, and out of the waves rose dim forms that did him homage. Before him lay his shadow, which was the body of his Soul, and behind him hung the moon in the honey-coloured air.

And his Soul said to him, "If indeed thou must drive me from thee, send me not forth without a heart. The world is cruel, give me thy heart to take with me."

He tossed his head and smiled, "With what should I love my love if I gave thee my heart?" he cried.

"Nay, but be merciful," said his Soul, "give me thy heart, for the world is very cruel, and I am afraid."

"My heart is my love's," he answered, "therefore tarry not, but get thee gone."

"Should I not love also?" asked his Soul.

"Get thee gone, for I have no need of thee," cried the young Fisherman, and he took the little knife with its handle of green viper skin, and cut away his shadow from around his feet, and it rose up and stood before him, and looked at him, and it was even as himself.

He crept back, and thrust the knife into his belt, and a feeling of awe came over him. "Get thee gone," he murmured, "and let me see thy face no more."

"Nay, but we must meet again," said the Soul. Its voice was low and flute-like and its lips hardly moved while it spake.

"How shall we meet?" cried the young Fisherman. "Thou wilt not follow me into the depths on the sea?"

"Once every year I will come to this place, and call to thee," said the Soul. "It may be that thou wilt have need of me."

"What need should I have of thee?" cried the young Fisherman, "but be it as thou wilt," and he plunged into the water, and the Tritons blew their horns, and the little Mermaid rose up to meet him, and put her arms around his neck and kissed him on the mouth.

And the Soul stood on the lonely beach, and watched them. And when they had sunk down into the sea, it went weeping away over the marshes.

And after a year was over the Soul came down to the shore of the sea and called to the young Fisherman, and he rose out of the deep, and said, "Why dost thou call to me?"

171

And the Soul answered, "Come nearer, that I may speak with thee, for I have seen marvellous things."

So he came nearer, and couched in the shallow water, and leaned his head upon his hand and listened.

And the Soul said to him, "When I left thee I turned my face to the East and journeyed. From the East cometh everything that is wise. Six days I journeyed, and on the morning of the seventh day I came to a hill that is in the country of the Tartars. I sat down under the shade of a tamarisk tree to shelter myself from the sun. The land was dry and burnt up with the heat. The people went to and fro over the plain like flies crawling upon a disk of polished copper.

"When it was noon a cloud of red dust rose up from the flat rim of the land. When the Tartars saw it, they strung their painted bows and having leapt upon their horses they galloped to meet it. The women fled screaming to the wagons, and hid themselves behind the felt curtains.

"At twilight the Tartars returned, but five of them were missing, and of those that came back not a few had been wounded. They harnessed their horses to the wagons and drove hastily away. Three jackals came out of a cave and peered after them. Then they sniffed up the air with their nostrils, and trotted off in the opposite direction.

"When the moon rose I saw a campfire burning on the plain, and went towards it. A company of merchants were seated round it on carpets. Their camels were picketed behind them, and the Negroes who were their servants were pitching tents of tanned skin upon the sand, and making a high wall of the prickly pear.

"As I came near them, the chief of the merchants rose up and drew his sword and asked me my business.

"I answered that I was a Prince in my own land, and that I had escaped the Tartars who sought to make me their slave. The chief smiled, and showed me five heads fixed upon long reeds of bamboo.

"Then he asked me who was the prophet of God, and I answered him Mohammed.

"When he heard the name of the false prophet, he bowed and

took me by the hand, and placed me by his side. A Negro brought me some mare's milk in a wooden dish, and a piece of roasted lamb.

"At daybreak we started on our journey. I rode on a red-haired camel by the side of the chief, and a runner ran before us carrying a spear. The men of war were on either hand, and the mules followed with the merchandise. There were forty camels in the caravan, and the mules were twice forty in number.

"We went from the country of the Tartars into the country of those who curse the Moon. We saw the Gryphons guarding their gold on the white rocks, and scaled Dragons sleeping in their caves. As we passed over the mountains we held our breath lest the snows might fall on us, and each man tied a veil of gauze before his eyes. As we passed through the valleys, the Pygmies shot arrows at us from the hollows of the trees, and at night-time we heard the wild men beating on their drums. When we came to the Tower of Apes, we set fruits before them, and they did not harm us. When we came to the Tower of Serpents, we gave them warm milk in bowls of brass, and they let us go by. Three times in our journey we came to the banks of the Oxus. We crossed it on rafts of wood with great bladders of blown hide. The river horses raged against us and sought to slay us. When the camels saw them they trembled.

"The kings of each city levied tolls on us, but would not suffer us to enter their gates. They threw us bread over the walls, little maizecakes baked in honey and cakes of fine flour filled with dates. For every hundred baskets we gave them a bead of amber.

"When the dwellers in the villages saw us coming, they poisoned the wells and fled to the hill-summits. We fought with the Magadae who are born old, and grow younger and younger every year, and die when they are little children; and with the Laktroi who say that they are the sons of tigers, and paint themselves yellow and black, and with the Aurantes who bury their dead on the tops of trees, and themselves live in dark caverns lest the Sun, who is their god, should slay them, and with the Krimnians who worship a crocodile, and give it earrings of green grass, and feed it with butter and fresh fowls; and with the Agazonbae, who are dogfaced; and with the

173

Sibans, who have horses' feet, and run more swiftly than horses. A third of our company died in battle, and a third died of want. The rest murmured against me, and said that I had brought them an evil fortune. I took a horned adder from beneath a stone and let it sting me. When they saw that I did not sicken they grew afraid.

"In the fourth month we reached the city of Illel. It was night-time when we came to the grove that is outside the walls, and the air was sultry, for the Moon was traveling in Scorpion. We took the ripe pomegranates from the trees, and brake them, and drank their sweet juices. Then we lay on our carpets and waited for the dawn.

"And at dawn we rose and knocked at the gate of the city. It was wrought out of red bronze, and carved with sea dragons and dragons that have wings. The guards looked down from the battlements and asked us our business. The interpreter of the caravan answered that we had come from the island of Syria with much merchandise. They took hostages, and told us that they would open the gate to us at noon, and bade us tarry till then.

"When it was noon they opened the gate, and as we entered in the people came crowding out of the houses to look at us, and a crier went round the city crying through a shell. We stood in the market-place, and the Negroes uncorded the bales of figured cloths and opened the carved chests of sycamore. And when they had ended their task, the merchants set forth their strange wares, the waxed linen from Egypt, and the painted linen from the country of the Ethiops, the purple sponges from Tyre and the blue hangings from Sidon, the cups of cold amber and the fine vessels of glass and the curious vessels of burnt clay. From the roof of a house a company of women watched us. One of them wore a mask of gilded leather.

"And on the first day the priests came and bartered with us, and on the second day came the nobles, and on the third day came the craftsmen and the slaves. And this is their custom with all merchants as long as they tarry in the city.

"And we tarried for a moon, and when the Moon was waning, I wearied and wandered away through the streets of the city and came to the garden of its god. The priests in their yellow robes moved silently through the green trees, and on a pavement of black marble stood the rose-red house in which the god had his dwelling. Its doors were of powdered lacquer, and bulls and peacocks were wrought on them in raised and polished gold. The tilted roof was of sea-green porcelain and the jutting eaves were festooned with little bells. When the white doves flew past, they struck the bells with their wings and made them tinkle.

"In front of the temple was a pool of clear water paved with veined onyx. I lay down beside it, and with my pale fingers I touched the broad leaves. One of the priests came towards me and stood behind me. He had sandals on his feet, one of soft serpent-skin and the other of birds' plumage. On his head was a mitre of black felt decorated with silver crescents. Seven yellows were woven into his robe, and his frizzed hair was stained with antimony.

"After a little while he spake to me, and asked me my desire.

"I told him that my desire was to see the god.

" 'The god is hunting,' said the priest, looking strangely at me with his small slanting eyes.

" 'Tell me in what forest, and I will ride with him,' I answered.

"He combed out the soft fringes of his tunic with his long pointed nails. 'The god is asleep,' he murmured.

" 'Tell me on what couch, and I will watch by him,' I answered.

" 'The god is at the feast,' he cried.

" 'If the wine be sweet I will drink it with him, and if it be bitter I will drink it with him also,' was my answer.

"He bowed his head in wonder, and taking me by the hand, he raised me up, and led me into the temple.

"And in the first chamber I saw an idol seated on a throne of jasper bordered with great orient pearls. It was carved out of ebony, and was of the stature of a man. On its forehead was a ruby, and thick oil dripped from its hair on to its thighs. Its feet were red with the blood of a newly-slain kid, and its loins girdled with a copper belt that was studded with seven beryls.

"And I said to the priest, 'Is this the god?' And he answered me, 'This is the god.'

175

"'Show me the god,' I cried, 'or I will surely slay thee.' And I touched his hand, and it became withered.

"And the priest besought me, saying, 'Let my lord heal his servant, and I will show him the god.'

"So I breathed with my breath upon his hand, and it became whole again, and he trembled and led me into the second chamber, and I saw an idol standing on a lotus of jade hung with great emeralds. It was carved out of ivory, and was twice the stature of a man. On its forehead was a chrysolite, and its breasts were smeared with myrrh and cinnamon. In one hand it held a crooked sceptre of jade, and in the other a round crystal. It wore buskins of brass, and its thick neck was circled with a circle of selenites.

"And I said to the priest, 'Is this the god?' And he answered me, 'This is the god.'

"'Show me the god,' I cried, 'or I will surely slay thee.' And I touched his eyes, and they became blind.

"And the priest besought me, saying, 'Let my lord heal his servant, and I will show him the god.'

"So I breathed with my breath upon his eyes, and the sight came back to them, and he trembled again, and led me into the third chamber, and lo! there was no idol in it, nor image of any kind, but only a mirror of round metal set on an altar of stone.

"And I said to the priest, 'Where is the god?'

"And he answered me: 'There is no god but this mirror that thou seest, for this is the Mirror of Wisdom. And it reflecteth all things that are in heaven and on earth, save only the face of him who looketh into it. This it reflecteth not, so that he who looketh into it may be wise. Many other mirrors are there, but they are mirrors of Opinion. This only is the Mirror of Wisdom. And they who possess this mirror know everything, nor is there anything hidden from them. And they who possess it not have not Wisdom. Therefore is it the god, and we worship it.' And I looked into the mirror, and it was even as he had said to me.

"And I did a strange thing, but what I did matters not, for in a valley that is but a day's journey from this place have I hidden the

Mirror of Wisdom. Do but suffer me to enter into thee again and be thy servant, and thou shalt be wiser than all the wise men, and Wisdom shall be thine. Suffer me to enter into thee, and none will be as wise as thou."

But the young Fisherman laughed. "Love is better than Wisdom," he cried, "and the little Mermaid loves me."

"Nay, but there is nothing better than Wisdom," said the Soul.

"Love is better," answered the young Fisherman, and he plunged into the deep, and the Soul went weeping away over the marshes.

And after the second year was over, the Soul came down to the shore of the sea, and called to the young Fisherman and he rose out of the deep, and said, "Why dost thou call to me?"

And the Soul answered, "Come nearer, that I may speak with thee, for I have seen marvellous things."

So he came nearer, and couched in the shallow water, and leaned his head upon his hand and listened.

And the Soul said to him, "When I left thee, I turned my face to the South and journeyed. From the South cometh everything that is precious. Six days I journeyed along the highways that lead to the city of Ashter, along the dusty red-dyed highways by which the pilgrims are wont to go did I journey, and on the morning of the seventh day I lifted my eyes, and lo! the city lay at my feet, for it is in a valley.

"There are nine gates to this city, and in front of each gate stands a bronze horse that neighs when the Bedouins come down from the mountains. The walls are cased with copper, and the watchtowers on the wall are roofed with brass. In every tower stands an archer with a bow in his hand. At sunrise he strikes with an arrow on a gong, and at sunset he blows through a horn of horn.

"When I sought to enter, the guards stopped me and asked of me who I was. I made answer that I was a Dervish and on my way to the city of Mecca, where there was a green veil on which the Koran was embroidered in silver letters by the hands of the angels. They were filled with wonder, and entreated me to pass in.

177

"Inside it is even as a bazaar. Surely thou shouldst have been with me. Across the narrow streets the gay lanterns of paper flutter like large butterflies. When the wind blows over the roofs they rise and fall as painted bubbles do. In front of their booths sit the merchants on silken carpets. They have straight black beards, and their turbans are covered with golden sequins, and long strings of amber and carved peach stones glide through their cool fingers. Some of them sell galbanum and nard, and curious perfumes from the islands of the Indian Sea, and the thick oil of red roses, and myrrh and little nail-shaped cloves. When one stops to speak to them, they throw pinches of frankincense upon a charcoal brazier and make the air sweet. I saw a Syrian who held in his hands a thin rod like a reed. Grey threads of smoke came from it, and its odour as it burned was as the odour of the pink almond in spring. Others sell silver bracelets embossed all over with creamy blue turquoise stones, and anklets of brass wire fringed with little pearls, and tigers' claws set in gold, and the claws of that gilt cat, the leopard, set in gold also, and earrings of pierced emerald, and finger rings of hollowed jade. From the tea-houses comes the sound of the guitar, and the opium smokers with their white smiling faces look out at the passers-by.

"Of a truth thou shouldst have been with me. The wine sellers elbow their way through the crowd with great black skins on their shoulders. Most of them sell the wine of Schiraz, which is as sweet as honey. They serve it in little metal cups and strew rose leaves upon it. In the marketplace stand the fruit sellers, who sell all kinds of fruit: ripe figs, with their bruised purple flesh, melons, smelling of musk and yellow as topazes, citrons and rose-apples and clusters of white grapes, round red-gold oranges, and oval lemons of green gold. Once I saw an elephant go by. Its trunk was painted with vermilion and turmeric, and over its ears it had a net of crimson silk cord. It stopped opposite one of the booths and began eating the oranges, and the man only laughed. Thou canst not think how strange a people they are. When they are glad they go to the bird sellers and buy of them a caged bird, and set it free that their joy may be greater, and when they are sad they scourge themselves with thorns that their sorrow may not grow less.

"One evening I met some Negroes carrying a heavy palanquin through the bazaar. It was made of gilded bamboo, and the poles were of vermilion lacquer studded with brass peacocks. Across the windows hung thin curtains of muslin embroidered with beetles' wings and with tiny seedpearls, and as it passed by a pale-faced Circassian looked out and smiled at me. I followed behind, and the Negroes hurried their steps and scowled. But I did not care. I felt a great curiosity come over me.

"At last they stopped at a square white house. There were no windows to it, only a little door like the door of a tomb. They set down the palanquin and knocked three times with a copper hammer. An Armenian in a caftan of green leather peered through the wicket, and when he saw them he opened, and spread a carpet on the ground, and the woman stepped out. As she went in, she turned round and smiled at me again. I had never seen any one so pale.

"When the moon rose I returned to the same place and sought for the house, but it was no longer there. When I saw that, I knew who the woman was, and wherefore she had smiled at me.

"Certainly thou shouldst have been with me. On the feast of the New Moon the young Emperor came forth from his palace and went into the mosque to pray. His hair and beard were dyed with rose leaves, and his cheeks were powdered with a fine gold dust. The palms of his feet and hands were yellow with saffron.

"At sunrise he went forth from his palace in a robe of silver, and at sunset he returned to it again in a robe of gold. The people flung themselves on the ground and hid their faces, but I would not do so. I stood by the stall of a seller of dates and waited. When the Emperor saw me, he raised his painted eyebrows and stopped. I stood quite still, and made him no obeisance. The people marveled at my boldness, and counselled me to flee from the city. I paid no heed to them, but went and sat with the sellers of strange gods, who by reason of their craft are abominated. When I told them what I had done, each of them gave me a god and prayed me to leave them.

"That night, as I lay on a cushion in the tea-house that is in the

Street of Pomegranates, the guards of the Emperor entered and led me to the palace. As I went in they closed each door behind me, and put a chain across it. Inside was a great court with an arcade running all round. The walls were of white alabaster, set here and there with blue and green tiles. The pillars were of green marble, and the pavement of a kind of peach-blossom marble. I had never seen anything like it before.

"As I passed across the court two veiled women looked down from a balcony and cursed me. The guards hastened on, and the butts of the lances rang upon the polished floor. They opened a gate of wrought ivory, and I found myself in a watered garden of seven terraces. It was planted with tulip cups and moonflowers, and silver-studded aloes. Like a slim reed of crystal a fountain hung in the dusky air. The cypress trees were like burnt-out torches. From one of them a nightingale was singing.

"At the end of the garden stood a little pavilion. As we approached it two eunuchs came out to meet us. Their fat bodies swayed as they walked, and they glanced curiously at me with their yellow-lidded eyes. One of them drew aside the captain of the guard, and in a low voice whispered to him. The other kept munching scented pastilles, which he took with an affected gesture out of an oval box of lilac enamel.

"After a few moments the captain of the guard dismissed the soldiers. They went back to the palace, the eunuchs following slowly behind and plucking the sweet mulberries from the trees as they passed. Once the elder of the two turned round, and smiled at me with an evil smile.

"Then the captain of the guard motioned me towards the entrance of the pavilion. I walked on without trembling, and drawing the heavy curtain aside I entered in.

"The young Emperor was stretched on a couch of dyed lion skins, and a ger-falcon perched upon his wrist. Behind him stood a brass-turbaned Nubian, naked down to the waist, and with heavy earrings in his split ears. On a table by the side of the couch lay a mighty scimitar of steel.

"When the Emperor saw me he frowned, and said to me:

" 'What is thy name? Knowest thou not that I am Emperor of this city?' But I made him no answer.

"He pointed with his finger at the scimitar, and the Nubian seized it, and rushing forward struck at me with great violence. The blade whizzed through me, and did me no hurt. The man fell sprawling on the floor, and when he rose up his teeth chattered with terror and he hid himself behind the couch.

"The Emperor leapt to his feet, and taking a lance from a stand of arms, he threw it at me. I caught it in its flight, and brake the shaft into two pieces. He shot at me with an arrow, but I held up my hands and it stopped in mid-air. Then he drew a dagger from a belt of white leather, and stabbed the Nubian in the throat lest the slave should tell of his dishonour. The man writhed like a trampled snake, and a red foam bubbled from his lips.

"As soon as he was dead the Emperor turned to me, and when he had wiped away the bright sweat from his brow, with a little napkin of purple silk, he said to me, 'Art thou a prophet, that I may not harm thee, or the son of a prophet, that I can do thee no hurt? I pray thee leave my city tonight, for while thou are in it I am no longer its lord.'

"And I answered him, 'I will go for half of thy treasure. Give me half of thy treasure, and I will go away.'

"He took me by the hand, and led me out into the garden. When the captain of the guard saw me, he wondered. When the eunuchs saw me, their knees shook and they fell upon the ground in fear.

"There is a chamber in the palace that has eight walls of red porphyry, and a brass-scaled ceiling hung with lamps. The Emperor touched one of the walls and it opened, and we passed down a corridor that was lit with many torches. In niches upon each side stood great wine jars filled to the brim with silver pieces. When we reached the centre of the corridor the Emperor spake the word that may not be spoken, and a granite door swung back on a secret spring, and he put his hands before his face lest his eyes should be dazzled.

"Thou couldst not believe how marvellous a place it was. There

181

were huge tortoise-shells full of pearls, and hollowed moonstones of great size piled up with red rubies. The gold was stored in coffers of elephant-hide, and the gold-dust in leather bottles. There were opals and sapphires, the former in cups of crystal, and the latter in cups of jade. Round green emeralds were ranged in order upon thin plates of ivory, and in one corner were silk bags filled, some with turquoise stones, and others with beryls. The ivory horns were heaped with purple amethysts, and the horns of brass with chalcedonies and sards. The pillars, which were of cedar, were hung with strings of yellow lynx-stones. In the flat oval shields there were carbuncles, both wine-coloured and coloured like grass. And yet I have told thee but a tithe of what was there.

"And when the Emperor had taken away his hands from before his face he said to me: 'This is my house of treasure, and half that is in it is thine, even as I promised to thee. And I will give thee camels and camel drivers, and they shall do thy bidding and take thy share of the treasure to whatever part of the world thou desirest to go. And the thing shall be done tonight, for I would not that the Sun, who is my father, should see that there is in my city a man whom I cannot slay.'

"But I answered him, 'The gold that is here is thine, and the silver also is thine, and thine are the precious jewels, and the things of price. As for me, I have no need of these. Nor shall I take aught from thee, but that little ring that thou wearest on the finger of thy hand.'

"And the Emperor frowned. 'It is but a ring of lead,' he cried, 'nor has it any value. Therefore take thy half of the treasure and go from my city.'

" 'Nay,' I answered, 'but I will take nought but that leaden ring, for I know what is written within it, and for what purpose.'

"And the Emperor trembled, and besought me and said, 'Take all the treasure and go from my city. The half that is mine shall be thine also.'

"And I did a strange thing, but what I did matters not, for in a cave that is but a day's journey from this place have I hidden the Ring of Riches. It is but a day's journey from this place, and it waits for thy coming. He who has this Ring is richer than all the kings of the world. Come therefore and take it, and the world's riches shall be thine."

But the young Fisherman laughed. "Love is better than Riches," he cried, "and the little Mermaid loves me."

"Nay, but there is nothing better than Riches," said the Soul.

"Love is better," answered the young Fisherman, and he plunged into the deep, and the Soul went weeping away over the marshes.

And after the third year was over, the Soul came down to the shore of the sea, and called to the young Fisherman, and he rose out of the deep and said, "Why dost thou call to me?"

And the Soul answered, "Come nearer, that I may speak with thee, for I have seen marvellous things."

So he came nearer, and couched in the shallow water, and leaned his head upon his hand and listened.

And the Soul said to him: "In a city that I know of there is an inn that standeth by a river. I sat there with sailors who drank of two different coloured wines, and ate bread made of barley, and little salt fish served in bay leaves with vinegar. And as we sat and made merry, there entered to us an old man bearing a leathern carpet and a lute that had two horns of amber. And when he had laid out the carpet on the floor, he struck with a quill on the wire strings of his lute, and a girl whose face was veiled ran in and began to dance before us. Her face was veiled with a veil of gauze, but her feet were naked. Naked were her feet, and they moved over the carpet like little white pigeons. Never have I seen anything so marvellous, and the city in which she dances is but a day's journey from this place."

Now when the young Fisherman heard the words of his Soul, he remembered that the little Mermaid had no feet and could not dance. And a great desire came over him, and he said to himself, "It is but a day's journey, and I can return to my love," and he laughed, and stood up in the shallow water, and strode towards the shore.

And when he had reached the dry shore he laughed again, and

held out his arms to his Soul. And his Soul gave a great cry of joy and ran to meet him, and entered into him, and the young Fisherman saw stretched before him upon the sand that shadow of the body that is the body of the Soul.

And his Soul said to him, "Let us not tarry, but get hence at once, for the Sea-gods are jealous, and have monsters that do their bidding."

So they made haste, and all that night they journeyed beneath the moon, and all the next day they journeyed beneath the sun, and on the evening of the day they came to a city.

And the young Fisherman said to his Soul, "Is this the city in which she dances of whom thou didst speak to me?"

And his Soul answered him, "It is not this city, but another. Nevertheless let us enter in."

So they entered in and passed through the streets, and as they passed through the Street of the Jewellers the young Fisherman saw a fair silver cup set forth in a booth. And his Soul said to him, "Take that silver cup and hide it."

So he took the cup and hid it in the fold of his tunic, and they went hurriedly out of the city.

And after they had gone a league from the city, the young Fisherman frowned, and flung the cup away, and said to his Soul, "Why didst thou tell me to take this cup and hide it, for it was an evil thing to do?"

But his Soul answered him, "Be at peace, be at peace."

And on the evening of the second day they came to a city, and the young Fisherman said to his Soul, "Is this the city in which she dances of whom thou didst speak to me?"

And his Soul answered him, "It is not this city, but another. Nevertheless let us enter in."

So they entered in and passed through the streets, and as they passed through the Street of the Sellers of Sandals, the young Fisherman saw a child standing by a jar of water. And his Soul said to him, "Smite that child." So he smote the child till it wept, and when he had done this they went hurriedly out of the city.

And after they had gone a league from the city the young Fisherman grew wroth, and said to his Soul, "Why didst thou tell me to smite the child, for it was an evil thing to do?"

But his Soul answered him, "Be at peace, be at peace."

And on the evening of the third day they came to a city, and the young Fisherman said to his Soul, "Is this the city in which she dances of whom thou didst speak to me?"

And his Soul answered him, "It may be that it is in this city, therefore let us enter in."

So they entered in and passed through the streets, but nowhere could the young Fisherman find the river or the inn that stood by its side. And the people of the city, looked curiously at him, and he grew afraid and said to his Soul, "Let us go hence, for she who dances with white feet is not here."

But his Soul answered, "Nay, but let us tarry, for the night is dark and there will be robbers on the way."

So he sat him down in the market-place and rested, and after a time there went by a hooded merchant who had a cloak of cloth of Tartary, and bore a lantern of pierced horn at the end of a jointed reed. And the merchant said to him, "Why dost thou sit in the market-place, seeing that the booths are closed and the bales corded?"

And the young Fisherman answered him, "I can find no inn in this city, nor have I any kinsman who might give me shelter."

"Are we not all kinsmen?" said the merchant. "And did not one God make us? Therefore come with me, for I have a guest-chamber."

So the young Fisherman rose up and followed the merchant to his house. And when he had passed through a garden of pomegranates and entered into the house the merchant brought him rosewater in a copper dish that he might wash his hands, and ripe melons that he might quench his thirst, and set a bowl of rice and a piece of roasted kid before him.

And after that he had finished, the merchant led him to the guest-chamber, and bade him sleep and be at rest. And the young Fisherman gave him thanks, and kissed the ring that was on his hand, and flung himself down on the carpets of dyed goat's hair. And when he had covered himself with a covering of black lamb's wool he fell asleep.

And three hours before dawn, and while it was still night, his Soul waked him and said to him, "Rise up and go to the room of the merchant, even to the room in which he sleepeth, and slay him, and take from him his gold, for we have need of it."

And the young Fisherman rose up and crept towards the room of the merchant, and over the feet of the merchant there was lying a curved sword, and the tray by the side of the merchant held nine purses of gold. And he reached out his hand and touched the sword, and when he touched it the merchant started and awoke, and leaping up seized himself the sword and cried to the young Fisherman, "Dost thou return evil for good, and pay with the shedding of blood for the kindness that I have shown thee?"

And his Soul said to the young Fisherman, "Strike him," and he struck him so that he swooned, and he seized then the nine purses of gold, and fled hastily through the garden of pomegranates, and set his face to the star that is the star of morning.

And when they had gone a league from the city, the young Fisherman beat his breast, and said to his Soul, "Why didst thou bid me slay the merchant and take his gold? Surely thou are evil."

But his Soul answered him, "Be at peace, be at peace."

"Nay," cried the young Fisherman, "I may not be at peace, for all that thou hast made me to do I hate. Thee also I hate, and I bid thee tell me wherefore thou hast wrought with me in this wise."

And his Soul answered him, "When thou didst send me forth into the world thou gavest me no heart, so I learned to do all these things and love them."

"What sayest thou?" murmured the young Fisherman.

"Thou knowest," answered his Soul, "thou knowest it well. Hast thou forgotten that thou gavest me no heart? I trow not. And so trouble not thyself nor me, but be at peace, for there is no pain that thou shalt not give away, nor any pleasure that thou shalt not receive."

And when the young Fisherman heard these words he trembled

and said to his Soul, "Nay, but thou art evil, and hast made me forget my love, and has tempted me with temptations, and hast set my feet in the ways of sins."

And his Soul answered him, "Thou hast not forgotten that when thou didst send me forth into the world thou gavest me no heart. Come, let us go to another city, and make merry, for we have nine purses of gold."

But the young Fisherman took the nine purses of gold and flung them down, and trampled on them.

"Nay," he cried, "but I will have nought to do with thee, nor will I journey with thee anywhere, but even as I sent thee away before, so will I send thee away now, for thou hast wrought me no good." And he turned his back to the moon, and with the little knife that had the handle of green viper skin he strove to cut from his feet that shadow of the body which is the body of the Soul.

Yet his Soul stirred not from him, nor paid heed to his command, but said to him, "The spell that the Witch told thee avails thee no more, for I may not leave thee, nor mayest thou drive me forth. Once in his life may a man send his Soul away, but he who receiveth back his Soul must keep it with him for ever, and this is his punishment and his reward."

And the young Fisherman grew pale and clenched his hands and cried, "She was a false Witch in that she told me not that."

"Nay," answered his Soul, "but she was true to Him she worships, and whose servant she will be ever."

And when the young Fisherman knew that he could no longer get rid of his Soul, and that it was an evil Soul, and would abide with him always, he fell upon the ground weeping bitterly.

And when it was day, the young Fisherman rose up and said to his Soul, "I will bind my hands that I may not do thy bidding, and close my lips that I may not speak thy words, and I will return to the place where she whom I love has her dwelling. Even to the sea will I return, and to the little bay where she is wont to sing, and I will call to her and tell her the evil I have done and the evil thou hast wrought on me."

And his Soul tempted him and said, "Who is thy love, that thou shouldst return to her? The world has many fairer than she is. There are the dancing girls of Samaris who dance in the manner of all kinds of birds and beasts. Their feet are painted with henna, and in their hands they have little copper bells. They laugh while they dance, and their laughter is as clear as the laughter of water. Come with me and I will show them to thee, for what is this trouble of thine about the things of sin? Is that which is pleasant to eat not made for the eater? Is there poison in that which is sweet to drink? Trouble not thyself but come with me to another city. There is a little city hard by in which there is a garden of tulip trees. And there dwell in this comely garden white peacocks and peacocks that have blue breasts. Their tails when they spread them to the sun are like disks of ivory and like gilt disks. And she who feeds them dances for pleasure, and sometimes she dances on her hands and at other times she dances with her feet. Her eyes are coloured with stibium, and her nostrils are shaped like the wings of a swallow. From a hook in one of her nostrils hangs a flower that is carved out of a pearl. She laughs while she dances, and the silver rings that are about her ankles tinkle like bells of silver. And so trouble not thyself anymore, but come with me to this city."

But the young Fisherman answered not his Soul, but closed his lips with the seal of silence and with a tight cord bound his hands, and journeyed back to the place from which he had come, even to the little bay where his love had been wont to sing. And ever did his Soul tempt him by the way, but he made it no answer, nor would he do any of the wickedness that it sought to make him do, so great was the power of the love that was within him.

And when he had reached the shore of the sea, he loosed the cord from his hands, and took the seal of silence from his lips and called to the Mermaid. But she came not to his call, though he called to her all day long and besought her.

And his Soul mocked him and said, "Surely thou hast but little joy out of thy love. Thou art as one who in time of death pours water into a broken vessel. Thou givest away what thou hast, and nought is given to thee in return. It were better for thee to come with me, for I know where the Valley of Pleasure lies, and what things are wrought there."

But the young Fisherman answered not his Soul, but in a cleft of the rock he built himself a house of wattles, and abode there for the space of a year. And every morning he called to the Mermaid, and every noon he called to her again, and at night-time he spake her name. Yet never did she rise out of the sea to meet him, nor in any place of the sea could he find her though he sought for her in the caves and in the green water, in the pools of the tide and in the wells that are at the bottom of the deep.

And ever did his Soul tempt him with evil, and whisper of terrible things. Yet did it not prevail against him, so great was the power of his love.

And after the year was over, the Soul thought within himself, "I have tempted my master with evil, and his love is stronger than I am. I will tempt him now with good, and it may be that he will come with me."

So he spake to the young Fisherman and said, "I have told thee of the joy of the world, and thou hast turned a deaf ear to me. Suffer me now to tell thee of the world's pain, and it may be that thou wilt hearken. For of a truth pain is the Lord of this world, nor is there any one who escapes from its net. There be some who lack raiment, and others who lack bread. There be widows who sit in purple, and widows who sit in rags. To and fro over the fens go the lepers, and they are cruel to each other. The beggars go up and down on the highways, and their wallets are empty. Through the streets of the cities walks Famine, and the Plague sits at their gates. Come, let us go forth and mend these things, and make them not to be. Wherefore shouldst thou tarry here calling to thy love, seeing she comes not to thy call? And what is love, that thou shouldst set this high store upon it?"

But the young Fisherman answered it nought, so great was the power of his love. And every morning he called to the Mermaid, and every noon he called to her again, and at night-time he spake her name. Yet never did she rise out of the sea to meet him, nor in any place of the sea could he find her, though he sought for her in the rivers of the sea, and in the valleys that are under the waves, in the sea that the night makes purple, and in the sea that the dawn leaves grey.

And after the second year was over, the Soul said to the young Fisherman at nighttime, and as he sat in the wattled house alone, "Lo! now I have tempted thee with evil, and I have tempted thee with good, and thy love is stronger than I am. Wherefore will I tempt thee no longer, but I pray thee to suffer me to enter thy heart, that I may be one with thee even as before."

"Surely thou mayest enter," said the young Fishermen, "for in the days when with no heart thou didst go through the world thou must have much suffered."

"Alas!" cried his Soul, "I can find no place of entrance, so compassed about with love is this heart of thine."

"Yet I would that I could help thee," said the young Fisherman.

And as he spake there came a great cry of mourning from the sea, even the cry that men hear when one of the Seafolk is dead. And the young Fisherman leapt up, and left his wattled house and ran down to the shore. And the black waves came hurrying to the shore, bearing with them a burden that was whiter than silver. White as the surf it was, and like a flower it tossed on the waves. And the surf took it from the waves, and the foam took it from the surf and the shore received it, and lying at his feet the young Fisherman saw the body of the little Mermaid. Dead at his feet it was lying.

Weeping as one smitten with pain he flung himself down beside it, and he kissed the cold red mouth, and toyed with the wet amber of the hair. He flung himself down beside it on the sand, weeping as one trembling with joy, and in his brown arms he held it to his breast. Cold were the lips, yet he kissed them. Salt was the honey of the hair, yet he tasted it with a bitter joy. He kissed the closed eyelids, and the wild spray that lay upon their cups was less salt than his tears.

And to the dead thing he made confession. Into the shells of its ears he poured the harsh wine of his tale. He put the little hands round his neck, and with his fingers he touched the thin reed of the throat. Bitter, bitter was his joy, and full of strange gladness was his pain.

The black sea came nearer, and the white foam moaned like a leper. With white claws of foam the sea grabbled at the shore. From the palace of the Sea King came the cry of mourning again, and far out upon the sea the great Tritons blew hoarsely upon their horns.

"Flee away," said his Soul, "for ever doth the sea come nigher, and if thou tarriest it will slay thee. Flee away, for I am afraid, seeing that thy heart is closed against me by reason of the greatness of thy love. Flee away to a place of safety. Surely thou wilt not send me without a heart into another world."

But the young Fisherman listened not to his Soul, but called on the little Mermaid and said, "Love is better than wisdom, and more precious than riches, and fairer than the feet of the daughters of men. The fires cannot destroy it, nor can the waters quench it. I called on thee at dawn, and thou didst not come to my call. The moon heard thy name, yet hadst thou no heed of me. For evilly had I left thee, and to my own hurt had I wandered away. Yet ever did thy love abide with me, and ever was it strong, nor did aught prevail against it, though I have looked upon evil and looked upon good. And now that thou art dead, surely I will die with thee also."

And his Soul besought him to depart, but he would not, so great was his love. And the sea came nearer, and sought to cover him with its waves, and when he knew that the end was at hand he kissed with mad lips the cold lips of the Mermaid, and the heart that was within him broke. And as through the fullness of his love his heart did break, the Soul found an entrance and entered in, and was one with him even as before. And the sea covered the young Fisherman with its waves.

And in the morning the Priest went forth to bless the sea, for it had been troubled. And with him went the monks and the musicians, and the candle bearers, and the swingers of censers, and a great company.

And when the Priest reached the shore he saw the young Fisherman lying drowned in the surf, and clasped in his arms was the body of the little Mermaid. And he drew back frowning, and having made the sign of the cross, he cried aloud and said, "I will not bless the sea nor anything that is in it. Accursed be the Sea-folk, and accursed be all they who traffic with them. And as for him who for love's sake forsook God, and so lieth here with his leman slain by God's judgment, take up his body and the body of his leman, and bury them in the corner of the Field of Fullers, and set no mark above them, nor sign of any kind, that none may know the place of their resting. For accursed were they in their lives, and accursed shall they be in their deaths also."

And the people did as he commanded them, and in the corner of the Field of Fullers, where no sweet herbs grew, they dug a deep pit, and laid the dead things within it.

And when the third year was over, and on a day that was a holy day, the Priest went up to the chapel, that he might show to the people the wounds of the Lord, and speak to them about the wrath of God.

And when he had robed himself with his robes, and entered in and bowed himself before the altar, he saw that the altar was covered with strange flowers that never had been seen before. Strange were they to look at, and of curious beauty, and their beauty troubled him, and their odour was sweet in his nostrils, and he felt glad, and understood not why he was glad.

And after that he had opened the tabernacle, and incensed the monstrance that was in it, and shown the fair wafer to the people, and hid it again behind the veil of veils, he began to speak to the people, desiring to speak to them of the wrath of God. But the beauty of the white flowers troubled him, and their odour was sweet in his nostrils, and there came another word into his lips, and he spoke not of the wrath of God, but of the God whose name is Love. And why he so spake he knew not.

And when he had finished his word the people wept, and the Priest went back to the sacristy, and his eyes were full of tears. And the deacons came in and began to unrobe him, and took from him the alb and the girdle, the maniple and the stole. And he stood as one in a dream.

And after that they had unrobed him, he looked at them and said, "What are the flowers, that stand on the altar, and whence do they come?"

And they answered him, "What flowers they are we cannot tell, but they come from the corner of the Fullers' Field." And the Priest trembled, and returned to his own house and prayed.

And in the morning, while it was still dawn, he went forth with the monks and the musicians, and the candle bearers and the swingers of censers, and a great company, and came to the shore of the sea, and blessed the sea, and all the wild things that are in it. The Fauns also he blessed, and the little things that dance in the woodland, and the bright-eyed things that peer through the leaves. All the things in God's world he blessed, and the people were filled with joy and wonder. Yet never again in the corner of the Fullers' Field grew flowers of any kind, but the field remained barren even as before. Nor came the Sea-folk into the bay as they had been wont to do, for they went to another part of the sea.

Tailpiece

Say not the mermaid is a myth,
I knew one once named Mrs. Smyth.
She stood while playing cards or knitting;
Mermaids are not equipped for sitting.